Student Solutions Manual

for use with

Elementary Statistics
A Brief Version

Second Edition

Allan G. Bluman
Community College of Allegheny County

Prepared by
Sally Robinson
South Plains College

Boston   Burr Ridge, IL   Dubuque, IA   Madison, WI   New York   San Francisco   St. Louis
Bangkok   Bogotá   Caracas   Lisbon   London   Madrid
Mexico City   Milan   New Delhi   Seoul   Singapore   Sydney   Taipei   Toronto

McGraw-Hill Higher Education

A Division of The McGraw-Hill Companies

Student Solutions Manual for use with
ELEMENTARY STATISTICS: A BRIEF VERSION, SECOND EDITION.
ALLAN G. BLUMAN.

Published by McGraw-Hill Higher Education, an imprint of The McGraw-Hill Companies, Inc.,
1221 Avenue of the Americas, New York, NY 10020. Copyright © The McGraw-Hill Companies,
Inc., 2003, 2000. All rights reserved.

This book is printed on acid-free paper.

2 3 4 5 6 7 8 9 0 DCD DCD 0 9 8 7 6 5 4 3 2

ISBN 0-07-242076-6

www.mhhe.com

Contents

Solutions to the Exercises

Preface

This manual includes solutions to odd and selected even exercises in *Elementary Statistics: A Brief Version*, Second Edition, by Allan G. Bluman. Solutions are worked out step-by-step where appropriate and generally follow the same procedures used in the examples in the textbook. Answers may be carried to several decimal places to increase accuracy and to facilitate checking. See your instructor for specific rounding rules. Graphs are included with the solutions when appropriate or required. They are intended to convey a general idea and may not be to scale.

To maximize the assistance provided in this manual, you should:

1. Read each section of the text carefully, noting examples and formulas.

2. Begin working the exercises using textbook examples and class notes as your guide, then refer to the answers in this manual.

3. Many instructors require students to interpret their answers within the context of the problem. These interpretations are powerful tools to understanding the meaning and purpose of each calculation. You should attempt to interpret each calculation even if you are not required to do so.

4. Be sure to show your work. When checking your work for errors you will need to review each step. When preparing for exams, reviewing each step helps you to recall the process involved in producing each calculation.

5. As you gain confidence and understanding, you should attempt to work exercises without referring to examples or notes. Check each answer in the solutions manual before beginning the next exercise.

6. Use a graphing calculator such as the TI-83 Plus for your calculations. Keep several decimal places throughout the calculation until you reach the final answer. Round your final answer if desired, and in accordance with your instructor's preferences.

7. Slight variations between your answers and the answers in this manual are probably due to rounding differences and should not be a cause for concern. If you are concerned about these variations, check each step of your calculation again.

8. Many errors can be traced to the improper application of the rules for order of operations. You should first attempt to determine where and how your error occurred because diagnosing your error increases understanding and prevents future errors. See your instructor if you are unsure of the location or cause of your error.

Sally H. Robinson

Chapter 1 - The Nature of Probability and Statistics

1-1. Descriptive statistics describes a set of data. Inferential statistics uses a set of data to make predictions about a population.

1-3. Answers will vary.

1-5. When the population is large, the researcher saves time and money using samples. Samples are used when the units must be destroyed.

1-6.
a. inferential   e. inferential
b. descriptive   f. inferential
c. descriptive   g. descriptive
d. descriptive   h. inferential

1-7.
a. ratio   f. nominal
b. ordinal   g. ratio
c. interval   h. ratio
d. ratio   i. ordinal
e. ratio   j. ratio

1-8.
a. qualitative   e. quantitative
b. quantitative   f. quantitative
c. qualitative   g. quantitative
d. quantitative

1-9.
a. discrete   e. continuous
b. continuous   f. continuous
c. discrete   g. discrete
d. continuous

1-11. Random samples are selected by using chance methods or random numbers. Systematic samples are selected by numbering each subject and selecting every kth number. Stratified samples are selected by dividing the population into groups and selecting from each group. Cluster samples are selected by using intact groups called clusters.

1-12.
a. cluster   d. systematic
b. systematic   e. stratified
c. random

1-13. Answers will vary.

1-15. Answers will vary.

1-17.
a. experimental   c. observational
b. observational   d. experimental

1-19. Answers will vary. Possible answers include:
(a) overall health of participants, amount of exposure to infected individuals through the workplace or home
(b) gender and/or age of driver, time of day
(c) diet, general health, heredity factors
(d) amount of exercise, heredity factors

1-21. Answers will vary.

1-23. Answers will vary.

CHAPTER QUIZ
1. True
2. False, it is a data value.
3. False, the highest level is ratio.
4. False, it is stratified sampling.
5. False, it is a quantitative variable.
6. True
7. False, it is 5.5-6.5 inches.
8. c.
9. b.
10. d.
11. a.
12. c.
13. a.
14. descriptive, inferential
15. gambling, insurance
16. population
17. sample

18.
a. saves time
b. saves money
c. use when population is infinite

19.
a. random   c. cluster
b. systematic   d. stratified

20. quasi-experimental

21. random

22.
a. inferential   d. descriptive
b. descriptive   e. inferential
c. inferential

1

23.
  a. ratio   d. ratio
  b. ordinal   e. nominal
  c. interval

24.
  a. continuous   d. continuous
  b. discrete   e. continuous
  c. discrete   f. discrete

25.
  a. 3.15-3.25   d. 0.265-0.275
  b. 17.5-18.5   e. 35.5-36.5
  c. 8.5-9.5

2-1. Frequency distributions are used to:
    1. organize data in a meaningful way
    2. determine the shape of the distribution
    3. facilitate computation procedures for finding descriptive measures such as the mean
    4. draw charts and graphs
    5. make comparisons between data sets

2-3.

a. $10.5 - 15.5$, $\frac{11+15}{2} = \frac{26}{2} = 13$, $15.5 - 10.5 = 5$

b. $16.5 - 39.5$, $\frac{17+39}{2} = \frac{56}{2} = 28$, $39.5 - 16.5 = 23$

c. $292.5 - 353.5$, $\frac{292+353}{2} = \frac{646}{2} = 323$, $353.5 - 292.5 = 61$

d. $11.75 - 14.75$, $\frac{11.75+14.75}{2} = \frac{26.5}{2} = 13.25$, $14.75 - 11.75 = 3$

e. $3.125 - 3.935$, $\frac{3.13+3.93}{2} = \frac{7.06}{2} = 3.53$, $3.935 - 3.125 = 0.81$

2-5.

a. Class width is not uniform.

b. Class limits overlap, and class width is not uniform.

c. A class has been omitted.

d. Class width is not uniform.

2-7.

Class	f
15130	5
15131	3
15132	3
15133	7
15134	2
	20

2-9.

Class	Boundaries	f
0	- 0.5 - 0.5	5
1	0.5 - 1.5	8
2	1.5 - 2.5	10
3	2.5 - 3.5	2
4	3.5 - 4.5	3
5	4.5 - 5.5	2
		30

2-11. H = 373 L = 21 R = 416 - 21 = 395
    W = 395 ÷ 12 = 32.9 or 33

2-11. continued

Limits	Boundaries	f	cf
21 - 53	20.5 - 53.5	2	2
54 - 86	53.5 - 86.5	0	2
87 - 119	86.5 - 119.5	1	3
120 - 152	119.5 - 152.5	1	4
153 - 185	152.5 - 185.5	2	6
186 - 218	185.5 - 218.5	10	16
219 - 251	218.5 - 251.5	9	25
252 - 284	251.5 - 284.5	9	34
285 - 317	284.5 - 317.5	5	39
318 - 350	317.5 - 350.5	4	43
351 - 383	350.5 - 383.5	5	48
384 - 416	383.5 - 416.5	1	49
		49	

2-13. H = 70 L = 27 R = 70 - 27 = 43
    W = 43 ÷ 7 = 6.1 or 7

Limits	Boundaries	f	cf
27 - 33	26.5 - 33.5	7	7
34 - 40	33.5 - 40.5	14	21
41 - 47	40.5 - 47.5	15	36
48 - 54	47.5 - 54.5	11	47
55 - 61	54.5 - 61.5	3	50
62 - 68	61.5 - 68.5	3	53
69 - 75	68.5 - 75.5	2	55
		55	

2-15.

Limits	Boundaries	f	cf
0 - 19	-0.5 - 19.5	13	13
20 - 39	19.5 - 39.5	18	31
40 - 59	39.5 - 59.5	10	41
60 - 79	59.5 - 79.5	5	46
80 - 99	79.5 - 99.5	3	49
100 - 119	99.5 - 119.5	1	50
		50	

2-17. H = 11,413 L = 150
    R = 11,413 - 150 = 11,263
    W = 11,263 ÷ 10 = 1126.3 or 1127

2-17. continued

Limits	Boundaries	f	cf
150 - 1276	149.5 - 1276.5	2	2
1277 - 2403	1276.5 - 2403.5	2	4
2404 - 3530	2403.5 - 3530.5	5	9
3531 - 4657	3530.5 - 4657.5	8	17
4658 - 5784	4657.5 - 5784.5	7	24
5785 - 6911	5784.5 - 6911.5	3	27
6912 - 8038	6911.5 - 8038.5	7	34
8039 - 9165	8038.5 - 9165.5	3	37
9166 - 10,292	9165.5 - 10,292.5	3	40
10,293 - 11,419	10,292.5 - 11,419.5	2	42
		42	

2-19.

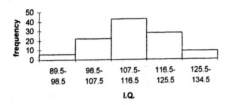

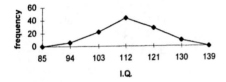

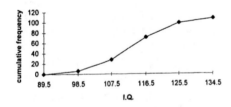

Eighty applicants do not need to enroll in the summer programs.

2-21.

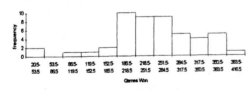

2-21. continued

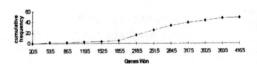

The majority of the pitchers won more than 185.5 games. There were no pitchers winning between 53.5 and 86.5 games.

2-23.

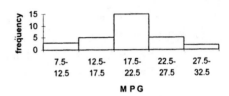

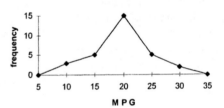

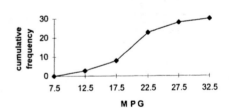

2-25.

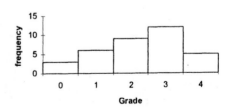

2-25. continued

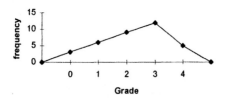

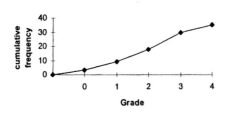

Yes, 26 out of the 35 students can enroll in the next course.

2-27.

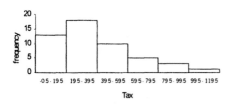

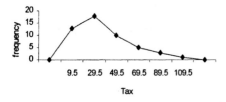

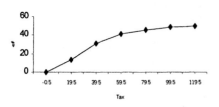

The majority of the states charge less than 40 cents per pack.

2-29.

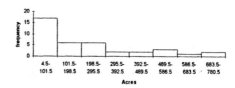

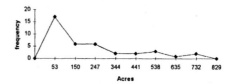

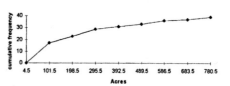

The highest number of parks had between 4.5 and 101.5 thousand acres.

2-31.

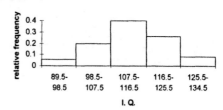

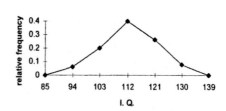

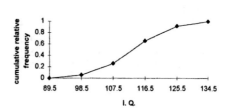

The proportion of applicants who need to enroll in a summer program is 0.26 or 26%.

2-33.

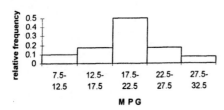

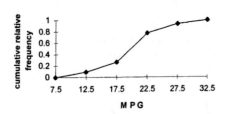

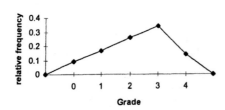

The proportion of automobiles that get 17.5 mpg or higher is 0.733 or 73.3%.

2-35.

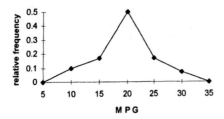

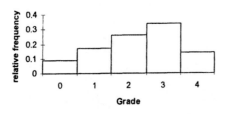

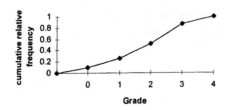

2-35. continued
The proportion of students who cannot meet the requirement for the next course is 0.26 or 26%.

2-37.

Limits	Boundaries	f	cf
22 - 24	21.5 - 24.5	1	1
25 - 27	24.5 - 27.5	3	4
28 - 30	27.5 - 30.5	0	4
31 - 33	30.5 - 33.5	6	10
34 - 36	33.5 - 36.5	5	15
37 - 39	36.5 - 39.5	3	18
40 - 42	39.5 - 42.5	2	20
		20	

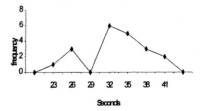

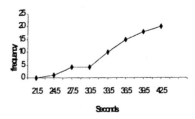

2-39.

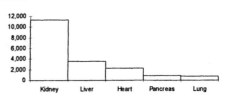

2-41.

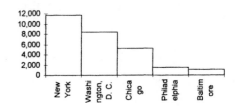

6

2-43.

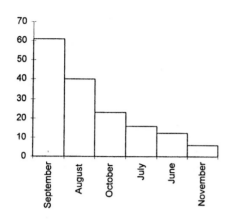

It would be advisable to avoid August and September, since these months have the most hurricanes.

2-45.

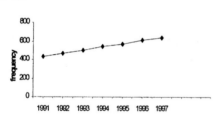

2-47.

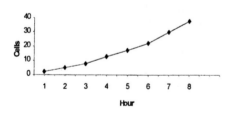

The number of cells began to increase rapidly after the third hour.

2-49.

Great Lakes	37	7.4%	27°
N. England	104	20.8%	75°
East Coast	206	41.2%	148°
South	96	19.2%	69°
West Coast	57	11.4%	41°
	500	100.0%	360°

2-49. continued

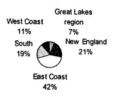

2-51.

Heart Disease	432	43.2%	155.5°
Cancer	227	22.7%	81.7°
Stroke	93	9.3%	33.5°
Accidents	24	2.4%	8.6°
Other	224	22.4%	80.6°
	1000	100.0%	360.0°

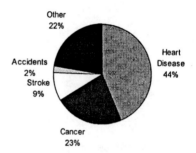

Yes, because comparisons could be make using the heights of the bars.

2-53.

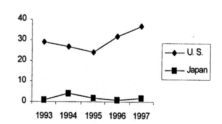

The United States has many more launches than Japan. The number of launches is relatively stable for Japan, while launches varied more for the U. S. The U. S. launches decreased slightly in 1995 and increased after that year.

2-55. scatter plot or scatter diagram

2-57. Two variables are positively related when the dependent variable, y, increases as the independent variable, x, increases. The

2-57. continued
points on the scatter plot fall approximately in an ascending straight line.

2-59.

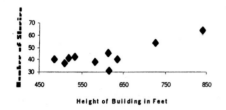

There appears to be a positive linear relationship between the height of a building and the number of stories in the building.

2-61.

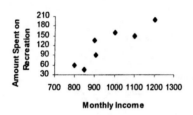

There appears to be a positive linear relationship between monthly income and amount spent on recreation.

2-63.

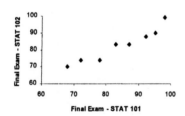

There appears to be a positive linear realationship between a student's final exam score in STAT 101 and STAT 102.

2-65.

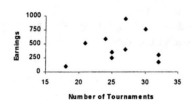

2-65. continued
There appears to be neither a positive nor negative linear relationship between the number of tournaments and the earnings of LPGA golfers.

2-67.

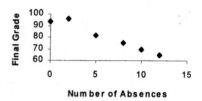

There appears to be a negative relationship between the number of absences and at student's final grade in a course.

2-69.

Class	f
Newspaper	7
Television	5
Radio	7
Magazine	6
	25

2-71.

Class	f
baseball	4
golf ball	5
tennis ball	6
soccer ball	5
football	5
	25

2-73.

Class	f	cf
11	1	1
12	2	3
13	2	5
14	2	7
15	1	8
16	2	10
17	4	14
18	2	16
19	2	18
20	1	19
21	0	19
22	1	20
	20	

2-75.

Limits	Boundaries	f	cf
1910 - 1919	1909.5 - 1919.5	1	1
1920 - 1929	1919.5 - 1929.5	2	3
1930 - 1939	1929.5 - 1939.5	15	18
1940 - 1949	1939.5 - 1949.5	12	30
1950 - 1959	1949.5 - 1959.5	20	50
1960 - 1969	1959.5 - 1969.5	18	68
1970 - 1979	1969.5 - 1979.5	18	86
1980 - 1989	1979.5 - 1989.5	6	92
1990 - 1999	1989.5 - 1999.5	8	100
		100	

2-77.

Limits	Boundaries	f	cf
170 - 188	169.5 - 188.5	11	11
189 - 207	188.5 - 207.5	9	20
208 - 226	207.5 - 226.5	4	24
227 - 245	226.5 - 245.5	5	29
246 - 264	245.5 - 264.5	0	29
265 - 283	264.5 - 283.5	0	29
284 - 302	283.5 - 302.5	0	29
303 - 321	302.5 - 321.5	1	30
		30	

2-79.

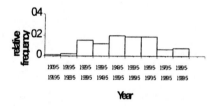

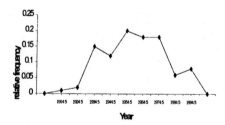

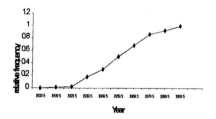

2-81.

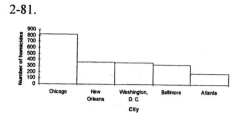

2-83.

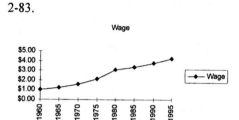

The minimum wage has increased over the years with the largest increase occurring between 1975 and 1980.

2-85.

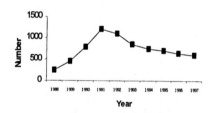

The sale of sports cards increased rapidly from 1988 to 1991, the declined from 1991 to 1997.

2-87.

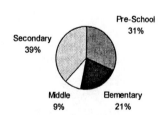

The fewest number of students were enrolled in the middle school field, and more students were in the secondary field than any other field.

2-89.

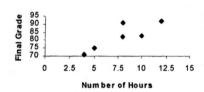

Number of Hours

There appears to be a positive linear relationship between the final grade a student receives and the number of hours of tutoring received by the student.

Chapter 2 Quiz
1. False
2. False
3. False
4. True
5. True
6. False
7. False
8. C
9. C
10. B
11. B
12. Categorical, ungrouped, grouped
13. 5, 20
14. categorical
15. time series
16. scatter plot
17. vertical or y
18.

	f
H	6
A	5
M	6
C	8
	25

19.

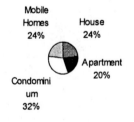

20.

Class	f	cf
0.5 − 1.5	1	1
1.5 − 2.5	5	6
2.5 − 3.5	3	9
3.5 − 4.5	4	13
4.5 − 5.5	2	15
5.5 − 6.5	6	21
6.5 − 7.5	2	23
7.5 − 8.5	3	26
8.5 − 9.5	4	30
	30	

21.

Items Purchased

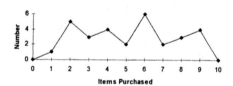

Items Purchased

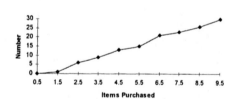

Items Purchased

22.

Class	Boundaries	mp	f	cf
102 − 116	101.5 − 116.5	109	4	4
117 − 131	116.5 − 131.5	124	3	7
132 − 146	131.5 − 146.5	139	1	8
147 − 161	146.5 − 161.5	154	4	12
162 − 176	161.5 − 176.5	169	11	23
177 − 191	176.5 − 191.5	184	7	30
			30	

23.

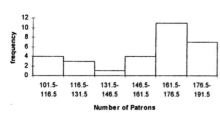

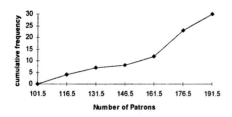

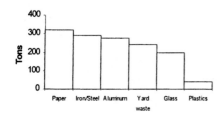

The distribution is somewhat U-shaped with a peak occurring in the 161.5 - 176.5 class.

24.

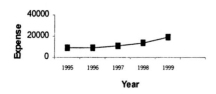

25.

The amount of money spent has increased every year and is more than twice what it was in 1995.

26.

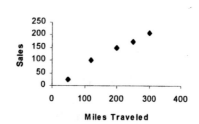

There appears to be a positive linear relationship between the number of miles traveled and the sales (in hundreds of dollars) of a sales representative.

Note to instructors: Answers may vary slightly due to rounding.

3-1.

$$\overline{X} = \frac{\sum X}{n} = \frac{8+12+15+9+6+8+10+9+8+6+7+8}{12} = \frac{106}{12} = 8.83$$

$$6, 6, 7, 8, 8, 8, \Big/ 8, 9, 9, 10, 12, 15$$
$$\qquad\qquad\quad \text{MD}$$

MD = 8   Mode = 8   MR = $\frac{L+H}{2} = \frac{6+15}{2} = 10.5$

3-3.

$$\overline{X} = \frac{\sum X}{n} = \frac{61+11+1+3+2+30+18+3+7}{9} = \frac{136}{9} = 15.1$$

$$1, 2, 3, 3, 7, 11, 18, 30, 61$$
$$\qquad\quad \uparrow \text{MD}$$

Mode = 3   MR = $\frac{L+H}{2} = \frac{1+61}{2} = 31$

The median is probably the best measure of average because 61 is an extremely large data value and makes the mean artificially high.

3-5.

$$\overline{X} = \frac{\sum X}{n} = \frac{150+110+100+35+60+130+40+140+120+160+110}{11} = \frac{1155}{11} = 105$$

$$35, 40, 60, 100, 110, 110, 120, 130, 140, 150, 160$$
$$\qquad\qquad\qquad\quad \uparrow \text{MD}$$

MD = 110   Mode = 110   MR = $\frac{L+H}{2} = \frac{35+160}{2} = 97.5$

3-7.

$$\overline{X} = \frac{7.0+7.2+6.2+5.4+7.7+6.4+6.2+6.5+8.0+7.2+6.4+5.4}{12} = \frac{79.6}{12} = 6.6$$

$$5.4, 5.4, 6.2, 6.2, 6.4, 6.4, \Big/ 6.5, 7.0, 7.2, 7.2, 7.7, 8.0$$
$$\qquad\qquad\qquad\qquad \text{MD}$$

MD = $\frac{6.4+6.5}{2} = 6.45$ Mode = none   MR = $\frac{L+H}{2} = \frac{5.4+8.0}{2} = 6.7$

3-9.

$$\overline{X} = \frac{\sum X}{n} = \frac{150+\cdots+11{,}413}{42} = 5678.9$$

$$150, 885, \cdots, 5315, \Big/ 5370, \cdots, 11{,}070, 11{,}413$$
$$\qquad\qquad\qquad\quad \uparrow \text{MD}$$

MD = $\frac{5315+5370}{2} = 5342.5$ Mode = 4450   MR = $\frac{L+H}{2} = \frac{150+11{,}413}{2} = 5781.5$

The distribution is skewed to the right.

3-11.
In 1995:

$$\overline{X} = \frac{24{,}911}{27} = 922.6$$

MD = 527   Mode = none   MR = $\frac{69+4192}{2} = 2130.5$

3-11. continued
In 1996:
$$\overline{X} = \frac{24,615}{2} = 911.7$$

$MD = 485$ $Mode = 1430$ $MR = \frac{70+4040}{2} = 2055$

The mean, median, and midrange of the traffic fatalities for 1996 are somewhat less than those for the 1995 fatalities, indicating that the number of fatalities decreased.

3-13.

Class Limits	Boundaries	X_m	f	$f \cdot X_m$	cf
$16 - 18$	$15.5 - 18.5$	17	20	340	20
$19 - 21$	$18.5 - 21.5$	20	18	360	38
$22 - 24$	$21.5 - 24.5$	23	8	184	46
$25 - 27$	$24.5 - 27.5$	26	4	104	50
			50	988	

207.5

$$\overline{X} = \frac{\sum f \cdot X_m}{n} = \frac{998}{50} = 19.76$$

modal class $= 15.5 - 18.5$

3-15.

Class	Boundaries	X_m	f	$f \cdot X_m$	cf
0 - 2	-0.5 - 2.5	1	2	2	2
3 - 5	2.5 - 5.5	4	6	24	8
6 - 8	5.5 - 8.5	7	12	84	20
9 - 11	8.5 - 11.5	10	5	50	25
12 - 14	11.5 - 14.5	13	3	39	28
			28	199	

$$\overline{X} = \frac{\sum f \cdot X_m}{n} = \frac{199}{28} = 7.1$$

modal class $= 5.5 - 8.5$

3-17.

Boundaries	X_m	f	$f \cdot X_m$	cf
$52.5 - 63.5$	58	6	348	6
$63.5 - 74.5$	69	12	828	18
$74.5 - 85.5$	80	25	2000	43
$85.5 - 96.5$	91	18	1638	61
$96.5 - 107.5$	102	14	1428	75
$107.5 - 118.5$	113	5	565	80
		80	6807	

$$\overline{X} = \frac{\sum f \cdot X_m}{n} = \frac{6807}{80} = 85.09$$

modal class $= 74.5 - 85.5$

3-19.

Class Limits	Boundaries	X_m	f	$f \cdot X_m$	cf
13 – 19	12.5 – 19.5	16	2	32	2
20 – 26	19.5 – 26.5	23	7	161	9
27 – 33	26.5 – 33.5	30	12	360	21
34 – 40	33.5 – 40.5	37	5	185	26
41 – 47	40.5 – 47.5	44	6	264	32
48 – 54	47.5 – 54.5	51	1	51	33
55 – 61	54.5 – 61.5	58	0	0	33
62 – 68	61.5 – 68.5	65	2	130	35
			35	1183	

$$\overline{X} = \frac{\sum f \cdot X_m}{n} = \frac{1183}{35} = 33.8$$

modal class = 26.5 – 33.5

3-21.

Boundaries	X_m	f	$f \cdot X_m$	cf
15.5 – 18.5	17	14	238	14
18.5 – 21.5	20	12	240	26
21.5 – 24.5	23	18	414	44
24.5 – 27.5	26	10	260	54
27.5 – 30.5	29	15	435	69
30.5 – 33.5	32	6	192	75
		75	1779	

$$\overline{X} = \frac{\sum f \cdot X_m}{n} = \frac{1779}{75} = 23.72$$

modal class = 21.5 – 24.5

3-23.

Limits	Boundaries	X_m	f	$f \cdot X_m$	cf
27 - 33	26.5 - 33.5	30	7	210	7
34 - 40	33.5 - 40.5	37	14	518	21
41 - 47	40.5 - 47.5	44	15	660	36
48 - 54	47.5 - 54.5	51	11	561	47
55 - 61	54.5 - 61.5	58	3	174	50
62 - 68	61.5 - 68.5	65	3	195	53
69 - 75	68.5 - 75.5	72	2	144	55
			55	2462	

$$\overline{X} = \frac{\sum f \cdot X_m}{n} = \frac{2462}{55} = 44.76$$

modal class = 40.5 – 47.5

3-25.

Limits	Boundaries	X_m	f	$f \cdot X_m$	cf
0 - 19	-0.5 - 19.5	9.5	13	123.5	13
20 - 39	19.5 - 39.5	29.5	18	531.0	31
40 - 59	39.5 - 59.5	49.5	10	495.0	41
60 - 79	59.5 - 79.5	69.5	5	347.5	46
80 - 99	79.5 - 99.5	89.5	3	268.5	49
100 - 119	99.5 - 119.5	109.5	1	109.5	50
			50	1875.0	

$$\overline{X} = \frac{\sum f \cdot X_m}{n} = \frac{1875}{50} = 37.5$$

modal class $= 19.5 - 39.5$

3-27.

$$\overline{X} = \frac{\sum w \cdot X}{\sum w} = \frac{3(3.33) + 3(3.00) + 2(2.5) + 2.5(4.4) + 4(1.75)}{3 + 3 + 2 + 2.5 + 4} = \frac{41.99}{14.5} = 2.9$$

3-29.

$$\overline{X} = \frac{\sum w \cdot X}{\sum w} = \frac{9(427000) + 6(365000) + 12(725000)}{9 + 6 + 12} = \frac{14,733,000}{27} = \$545,666.67$$

3-31.

$$\overline{X} = \frac{\sum w \cdot X}{\sum w} = \frac{1(62) + 1(83) + 1(97) + 1(90) + 2(82)}{6} = \frac{496}{6} = 82.67$$

3-33.
a. Median
b. Mean
c. Mode
d. Mode
e. Mode
f. Mean

3-35.
Greek letters, μ

3-37.
$5 \cdot 8.2 = 41$
$6 + 10 + 7 + 12 + x = 41$
$x = 6$

3-39.
a. $\frac{2}{\frac{1}{30} + \frac{1}{45}} = 36$ mph

b. $\frac{2}{\frac{1}{40} + \frac{1}{25}} = 30.77$ mph

c. $\frac{2}{\frac{1}{50} + \frac{1}{10}} = \$16.67$

3-41.

$$\sqrt{\frac{8^2 + 6^2 + 3^2 + 5^2 + 4^2}{5}} = \sqrt{30} = 5.48$$

3-43.
The square root of the variance is equal to the standard deviation.

3-45.
σ^2, σ

3-47.
When the sample size is less than 30, the formula for the true standard deviation of the sample will underestimate the population standard deviation.

3-49.
R = 15 − 6 = 9

$$s^2 = \frac{\sum X^2 - \frac{(\sum X)^2}{n}}{n-1} = \frac{1209 - \frac{(117)^2}{12}}{12-1} = \frac{68.25}{11} = 6.20$$

$$s = \sqrt{6.20} = 2.5$$

3-51.
R = 10 − 0 = 10

$$s^2 = \frac{\sum X^2 - \frac{(\sum X)^2}{n}}{n-1} = \frac{423 - \frac{63^2}{15}}{15-1} = \frac{158.4}{14} = 11.3$$

$$s = \sqrt{11.3} = 3.4$$

3-53.
R = 46 − 16 = 30

$$s^2 = \frac{\sum X^2 - \frac{(\sum X)^2}{n}}{n-1} = \frac{9677 - \frac{313^2}{11}}{11-1} = \frac{770.727}{10} = 77.07$$

$$s = \sqrt{77.07} = 8.8$$

3-55.
R = 12 − 7 = 5

$$s^2 = \frac{\sum X^2 - \frac{(\sum X)^2}{n}}{n-1} = \frac{1958.56 - \frac{204^2}{22}}{22-1} = \frac{66.92}{21} = 3.2$$

$$s = \sqrt{3.2} = 1.8$$

3-57.
For 1995:
R = 4192 − 69 = 4123

$$s^2 = \frac{\sum X^2 - \frac{(\sum X)^2}{n}}{n-1} = \frac{49,784,885 - \frac{24,911^2}{27}}{27-1} = 1,030,817.63$$

$$s = \sqrt{1,030,817.63} = 1015.3$$

For 1996:
R = 4040 − 70 = 3970

$$s^2 = \frac{\sum X^2 - \frac{(\sum X)^2}{n}}{n-1} = \frac{48,956,875 - \frac{24,615^2}{27}}{27-1} = 1,019,853.85$$

3-57. continued
$$s = \sqrt{1,019,853.85} = 1009.9$$

The fatalities in 1995 are more variable.

3-59.
$$R = 11,413 - 150 = 11,263$$

$$s^2 = \frac{\sum X^2 - \frac{(\sum x)^2}{n}}{n-1} = \frac{1,659,371,050 - \frac{238,512^2}{42}}{42-1} = \frac{304,895,475.1}{41} = 7,436,475.003$$

$$s = \sqrt{7,436,475.003} = 2726.99$$

3-61.

X_m	f	$f \cdot X_m$	$f \cdot X_m^2$
16	2	32	512
23	7	161	3703
30	12	360	10800
37	5	185	6845
44	6	264	11616
51	1	51	2601
58	0	0	0
65	2	130	8450
	35	1183	44527

$$s^2 = \frac{\sum f \cdot X_m^2 - \frac{(\sum f \cdot X_m)^2}{n}}{n-1} = \frac{44,527 - \frac{1183^2}{35}}{35-1} = \frac{4541.6}{34} = 133.58$$

$$s = \sqrt{133.58} = 11.6$$

3-63.

Class	X_m	f	$f \cdot X_m$	$f \cdot X_m^2$
0 - 2	1	1	1	1
3 - 5	4	3	12	48
6 - 8	7	5	35	245
9 - 11	10	14	140	1400
12 - 14	13	6	78	1014
		29	266	2708

$$s^2 = \frac{\sum f \cdot X^2 - \frac{(\sum f \cdot x)^2}{n}}{n-1} = \frac{2708 - \frac{266^2}{29}}{29-1} = \frac{268.1379}{28} = 9.58$$

$$s = \sqrt{9.58} = 3.1$$

3-65.

X_m	f	$f \cdot X_m$	$f \cdot X_m^2$
58	6	348	20184
69	12	828	57132
80	25	2000	160000
91	18	1638	148058
102	14	1428	145656
112	5	565	63845
	80	6807	595875

$$s^2 = \frac{\sum f \cdot X_m^2 - \frac{(\sum f \cdot X_m)^2}{n}}{n-1} = \frac{595875 - \frac{6807^2}{80}}{80-1} = \frac{16684.39}{79} = 211.2$$

$$s = \sqrt{211.2} = 14.5$$

3-67.

X_m	f	$f \cdot X_m$	$f \cdot X_m^2$
56	2	112	6272
61	5	305	18605
66	8	528	34848
71	0	0	0
76	4	306	23104
81	5	405	32805
86	1	86	7396
	25	1740	123030

$$s^2 = \frac{\sum f \cdot X_m^2 - \frac{(\sum f \cdot X_m)^2}{n}}{n-1} = \frac{123030 = \frac{1740^2}{25}}{25-1} = \frac{1926}{24} = 80.3$$

$$s = \sqrt{80.25} = 9.0$$

3-69.

X_m	f	$f \cdot X_m$	$f \cdot X_m^2$
27	5	135	3645
30	9	270	8100
33	32	1056	34848
36	30	720	25920
39	12	468	18252
62	2	84	3528
	80	2733	94293

$$s^2 = \frac{\sum f \cdot X_m^2 - \frac{(\sum f \cdot X_m)^2}{n}}{n-1} = \frac{94293 - \frac{2733^2}{80}}{80-1} = \frac{926.89}{79} = 11.7$$

$$s = \sqrt{11.7} = 3.4$$

3-71.

C. Var $= \frac{s}{\overline{X}} = \frac{4,000}{40,000} = 0.10 = 10\%$

C. Var $= \frac{s}{\overline{X}} = \frac{2,000}{20,000} = 0.10 = 10\%$
They are equal.

3-73.

C. Var $= \frac{s}{\overline{X}} = \frac{6}{26} = 0.231 = 23.1\%$

3-73. continued

C. Var $= \frac{s}{\overline{X}} = \frac{4000}{31,000} = 0.129 = 12.9\%$

The age is more variable.

3-75.

a. $1 - \frac{1}{5^2} = 0.96$ or 96%

b. $1 - \frac{1}{4^2} = 0.9375$ or 93.75%

3-77.

$\overline{X} = 5.02$ $s = 0.09$

At least 75% of the data values will fall withing two standard deviations of the mean; hence, $2(\$0.09) = \$0.18$ and $\$5.02 - \$0.18 = \$4.84$ and $\$5.02 + \$0.18 = \$5.20$. Hence at least 75% of the data values will fall between $4.84 and $5.20.

3-79.

$\overline{X} = 95$ $s = 2$

At least 88.89% of the data values will fall within 3 standard deviations of the mean, hence $95 - 3(2) = 89$ and $95 + 3(2) = 101$. Therefore at least 88.89% of the data values will fall between 89 mg and 101 mg.

3-81.

$\overline{X} = 12$ $s = 3$

$20 - 12 = 8$ and $8 \div 3 = 2.67$

Hence, $1 - \frac{1}{k^2} = 1 - \frac{1}{2.67^2} = 1 - 0.14 = 0.86 = 86\%$

At least 86% of the data values will fall between 4 and 20.

3-83.

$n = 30$ $\overline{X} = 214.97$ $s = 20.76$ At least 75% of the data values will fall between $\overline{X} \pm 2s$.

$\overline{X} - 2(20.76) = 214.97 - 41.52 = 173.45$ and $\overline{X} + 2(20.76) = 214.97 + 41.52 = 256.49$

In this case all 30 values fall within this range; hence Chebyshev's Theorem is correct for this example.

3-85.

For $k = 1.5$, $1 - \frac{1}{1.5^2} = 1 - 0.44 = 0.56$ or 56%

For $k = 2$, $1 - \frac{1}{2^2} = 1 - 0.25 = 0.75$ or 75%

For $k = 2.5$, $1 - \frac{1}{2.5^2} = 1 - 0.16 = 0.84$ or 84%

For $k = 3$, $1 - \frac{1}{3^2} = 1 - 0.1111 = .8889$ or 88.89%

For $k = 3.5$, $1 - \frac{1}{3.5^2} = 1 - 0.08 = 0.92$ or 92%

3-87.

$\overline{X} = 13.3$

Mean Dev $= \frac{|5-13.3|+|9-13.3|+|10-13.3|+|11-13.3|+|11-13.3|}{10}$

$+ \frac{|12-13.3|+|15-13.3|+|18-13.3|+|20-13.3|+|22-13.3|}{10} = 4.36$

3-89.

A z score tells how many standard deviations the data value is above or below the mean.

3-91.

A percentile is a relative measure while a percent is an absolute measure of the part to the total.

3-93.
$Q_1 = P_{25}, \; Q_2 = P_{50}, \; Q_3 = P_{75}$

3-95.
$D_1 = P_{10}, \; D_2 = P_{20}, \; D_3 = P_{30}$, etc

3-97.
a. $z = \frac{X-\overline{X}}{s} = \frac{115-100}{10} = 1.5$

b. $z = \frac{124-100}{10} = 2.4$

c. $z = \frac{93-100}{10} = -0.7$

d. $z = \frac{100-100}{10} = 0$

e. $z = \frac{85-100}{10} = -1.5$

3-99.
a. $z = \frac{X-\overline{X}}{s} = \frac{87-84}{4} = 0.75$

b. $z = \frac{79-84}{4} = -1.25$

c. $z = \frac{93-84}{4} = 2.25$

d. $z = \frac{76-84}{4} = -2$

e. $z = \frac{82-84}{4} = -0.5$

3-101.
a. $z = \frac{43-40}{3} = 1$

b. $z = \frac{75-72}{5} = 0.6$

a is higher

3-103.
a. $z = \frac{3.2-4.6}{1.5} = -0.93$ b. $z = \frac{630-800}{200} = -0.85$ c. $z = \frac{43-50}{5} = -1.4$

B is the highest

3-105.
a. 21st b. 58th c. 77th d. 29th

3-106.
a. 7   b. 25   c. 64   d. 76   e. 93

3-107.
a. a. 235   b. 255   c. 261   d. 275   e. 283

3-108.
a. 376   b. 410   c. 446   d. 473   e. 498

Chapter 3 - Data Description

3-109.
a. 17th   b. 39th   c. 53rd   d. 79th   e. 91st

3-111.
$c = \frac{6(30)}{100} = 1.8$ or 2   82

3-113.
$c = \frac{n \cdot p}{100} = \frac{7(60)}{100} = 4.2$ or 5   Hence, 47 is the closest value to the 60th percentile.

3-115.
$c = \frac{6(33)}{100} = 1.98$ or 2   5, 12, 15, 16, 20, 21
$\uparrow P_{33}$

3-117.
a. 5, 12, 16, 25, 32, 38 $Q_1 = 12$ and $Q_3 = 32$

Midquartile = $\frac{12+32}{2} = 22$ Interquartile range: $32 - 12 = 20$

b. 53, 62, 78, 94, 96, 99, 103 $Q_1 = 62$ and $Q_3 = 99$

Midquartile = $\frac{62+99}{2} = 80.5$ Interquartile range: $99 - 62 = 37$

3-119.
Stem and leaf plot, median, and interquartile range

3-121.
A resistant statistic is relatively less affected by outliers than a non-resistant statistic.

3-123.
```
3 | 8
4 | 1
5 | 0 0 2 3 3 6 8 9
6 | 6 8 9 9
7 | 0 0 3 4 5 8
8 | 0 1 3 3 4 4 4 5 7 9 9 9
9 | 0 2 4
```
The majority of automobile thefts occurred in the 50's and 80's . The data is grouped towards the higher end of the distribution.

3-125.

Females					Males			
			5	0	3			
				1	5 9			
				2	2			
7 4 3 2	0	3	1 1					
		6	4	1 4 6 6				
9 6 3	0	5	2 6 6 6 9					
	8 5	6	0 0 6 6					
7 2	0	7	7					
8 7 6 6 0	0	8	7 8					
4 2	9	6 8						

The distribution for unemployed males is more variable than the distribution for unemployed females. There are more unemployed females than males world-wide.

21

3-127.

$MD = \frac{3.9+4.7}{2} = 4.3$

$Q_1 = 2.0 \quad Q_3 = 7.6$

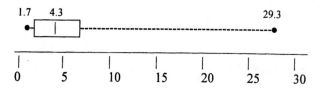

The distribution is positively skewed.

3-129.

For 1993: $MD = \frac{11+13}{2} = 12$

$Q_1 = \frac{7+9}{2} = 8 \qquad Q_3 = \frac{13+13}{2} = 13$

For 1970: $MD = \frac{5+6}{2} = 5.5$

$Q_1 = \frac{4+5}{2} = 4.5 \qquad Q_3 = \frac{7+8}{2} = 7.5$

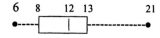

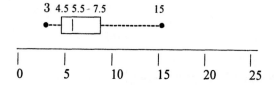

The divorce rates are higher and more variable in 1993 than in 1970.

3-131.

a. $\overline{X} = \dfrac{\sum X}{n} = \dfrac{2343+1240+1088+600+497+1925+1480+458}{8} = 1203.9$

b. 458 497 600 1088 1240 1480 1925 2343

$$MD = \frac{1088+1240}{2} = 1164$$

c. no mode

d. $MR = \frac{458+2343}{2} = 1400.5$

e. Range $= 2343 - 458 = 1885$

f. $s^2 = \dfrac{\sum X^2 - \frac{(\sum x)^2}{n}}{n-1} = \dfrac{14{,}923{,}791 - \frac{9631^2}{8}}{8-1} = 475{,}610.1$

g. $s = \sqrt{475{,}610.1} = 689.6$

3-133.

Class	X_m	f	$f \cdot X_m$	$f \cdot X_m^2$	cf
1 - 3	2	1	2	4	1
4 - 6	5	4	20	100	5
7 - 9	8	5	40	320	10
10 - 12	11	1	11	121	11
13 - 15	14	1	14	196	12
		12	87	741	

a. $\overline{X} = \dfrac{\sum f \cdot X_m}{n} = \dfrac{87}{12} = 7.25$

b. Modal Class = 7 - 9 or 6.5 - 9.5

c. $s^2 = \dfrac{741 - \frac{87^2}{12}}{11} = \dfrac{110.25}{11} = 10.0$

f. $s = \sqrt{10.0} = 3.2$

3-135.

Class Boundaries	X_m	f	$f \cdot X_m$	$f \cdot X_m^2$	cf
12.5 - 27.5	20	6	120	2400	6
27.5 - 42.5	35	3	105	3675	9
42.5 - 57.5	50	5	250	12,500	14
57.5 - 72.5	65	8	520	33,800	22
72.5 - 87.5	80	6	480	38,400	28
87.5 - 102.5	95	2	190	18,050	30
		30	1665	108,825	

a. $\overline{X} = \dfrac{\sum f \cdot X_m}{n} = \dfrac{1665}{30} = 55.5$

b. Modal class $= 57.5 - 72.5$

c. $s^2 = \dfrac{\sum f \cdot X_m^2 - \frac{(\sum f \cdot X_m)^2}{n}}{n-1} = \dfrac{108825 - \frac{1665^2}{30}}{30-1} = \dfrac{16417.5}{29} = 566.1$

d. $s = \sqrt{566.1} = 23.8$

3-137.

$\overline{X} = \dfrac{\sum w \cdot X}{\sum w} = \dfrac{12 \cdot 0 + 8 \cdot 1 + 5 \cdot 2 + 5 \cdot 3}{12 + 8 + 5 + 5} = \dfrac{33}{30} = 1.1$

3-139.

$\overline{X} = \dfrac{\sum w \cdot X}{\sum w} = \dfrac{8 \cdot 3 + 1 \cdot 6 + 1 \cdot 30}{8 + 1 + 1} = \dfrac{60}{10} = 6$

3-141.

C. Var $= \dfrac{s}{\overline{X}} = \dfrac{12}{56} = 0.214$

C. Var $= \dfrac{s}{\overline{X}} = \dfrac{2.5}{6} = 0.417$

The number of years is more variable.

3-143.

a.

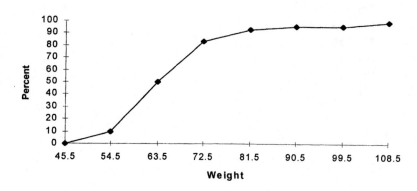

b. $P_{35} = 60$; $P_{65} = 67$; $P_{85} = 75$

c. $48 \Rightarrow 4^{th}$ percentile; $54 \Rightarrow 9^{th}$ percentile; $62 \Rightarrow 42^{nd}$ percentile

3-145.

$\overline{X} = 0.32$ $s = 0.03$ $k = 2$

$0.32 - 2(0.03) = 0.26$ and $0.32 + 2(0.03) = 0.38$

At least 75% of the values will fall between \$0.26 and \$0.38.

3-147.

$\overline{X} = 54$ $s = 4$ $60 - 54 = 6$ $k = \frac{6}{4} = 1.5$ $1 - \frac{1}{1.5^2} = 1 - 0.44 = 0.56$ or 56%

3-149.

$\overline{X} = 32$ $s = 4$ $44 - 32 = 12$ $k = \frac{12}{4} = 3$ $1 - \frac{1}{3^2} = 0.8889 = 88.89\%$

3-151.

```
2 | 9 9
3 | 2 4 5 6 8 8
4 | 1 2 3 7 7
5 | 1 3 5 8
6 | 2 2 2 3 7
7 | 2 3
```

3-153.

```
20 | 0 4 9
21 | 0 1 2 7 8 8
22 | 2 7 7 7 8
23 | 0 1 3 7 8
24 | 1 2 2 3 7
25 | 1 1 3 4 6
26 | 0
```

Quiz

1. True
2. False
3. False
4. False
5. False
6. False
7. False

8. False
9. False
10. c.
11. c.
12. a and b
13. b.
14. d.
15. b.
16. statistic
17. parameters, statistics
18. standard deviation
19. σ
20. midrange
21. positively
22. outlier
23. a. 84.1   b. 85   c. none   d. 84   e. 12   f. 17.1   g. 4.1
24. a. 6.4   b. 5.5 - 8.5   c. 11.6   d. 3.4
25. a. 51.4   b. 35.5 - 50.5   c. 451.5   d. 21.3
26. a. 8.2   b. 6.5 - 9.5   c. 21.6   d. 4.6
27. 1.6
28. 4.46
29. 0.33; 0.162; newspapers
30. 0.3125; 0.229; brands
31. -0.75; -1.67; science
32. a. 0.5   b. 1.6   c. 15, c is higher
33. a. 6; 19; 31; 44; 56; 69; 81; 94   b. 27
   c.

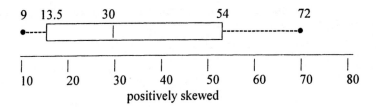

positively skewed

34.
a.

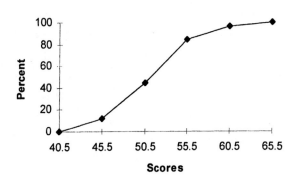

b. 47; 55; 65
c. 60th percentile; 6th percentile; 98th percentile

35.

```
1 | 5  9
2 | 6  8
3 | 1  5  8  8  9
4 | 1  7  8
5 | 3  3  4
6 | 2  3  7  8
7 | 6  9
8 | 6  8  9
9 | 8
```

36.
For 1997:
MD = 158 $Q_1 = 101$ $Q_3 = 589$

For 1998:
MD = 154 $Q_1 = 107$ $Q_3 = 627$

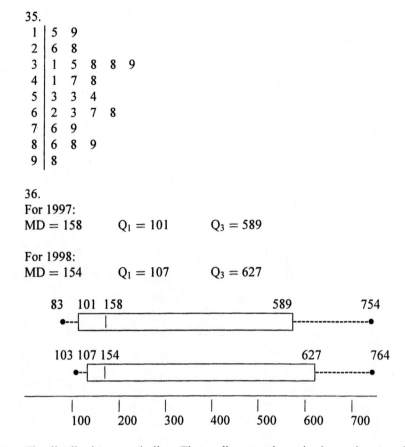

The distributions are similar. The median attendance is almost the same for both years. The range in attendance is slightly larger for 1997.

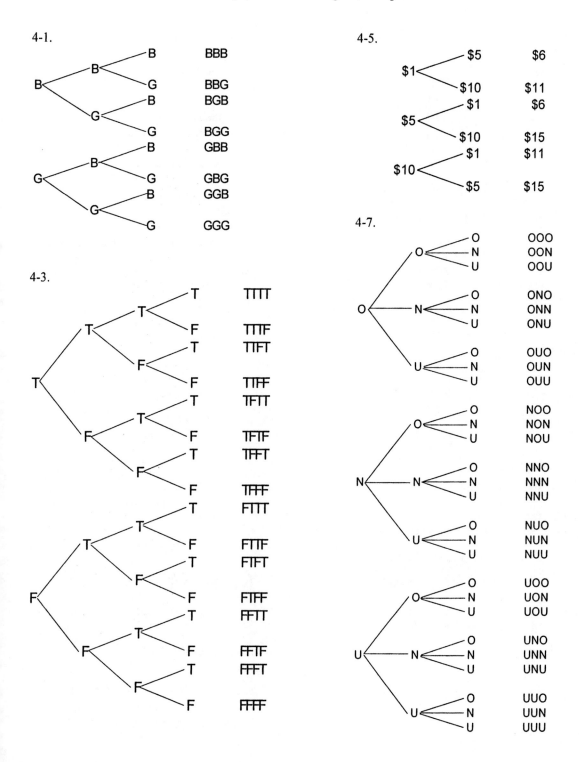

4-1.

		B	BBB
	B	G	BBG
B		B	BGB
	G	G	BGG
		B	GBB
	B	G	GBG
G		B	GGB
	G	G	GGG

4-5.

	$5	$6
$1	$10	$11
	$1	$6
$5	$10	$15
	$1	$11
$10	$5	$15

4-3.

		T	TTTT
	T	F	TTTF
T		T	TTFT
	F	F	TTFF
		T	TFTT
	T	F	TFTF
F		T	TFFT
	F	F	TFFF
		T	FTTT
	T	F	FTTF
T		T	FTFT
	F	F	FTFF
		T	FFTT
	T	F	FFTF
F		T	FFFT
	F	F	FFFF

4-7.

		O	OOO
	O	N	OON
		U	OOU
		O	ONO
O	N	N	ONN
		U	ONU
		O	OUO
	U	N	OUN
		U	OUU
		O	NOO
	O	N	NON
		U	NOU
		O	NNO
N	N	N	NNN
		U	NNU
		O	NUO
	U	N	NUN
		U	NUU
		O	UOO
	O	N	UON
		U	UOU
		O	UNO
U	N	N	UNN
		U	UNU
		O	UUO
	U	N	UUN
		U	UUU

4-9.

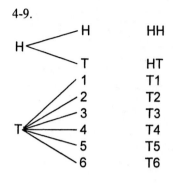

HH
HT
T1
T2
T3
T4
T5
T6

4-11.

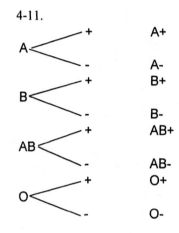

A+
A-
B+
B-
AB+
AB-
O+
O-

4-13.
$10^5 = 100,000$
$10 \cdot 9 \cdot 8 \cdot 7 \cdot 6 = 30,240$

4-15.
$7! = 7 \cdot 6 \cdot 5 \cdot 4 \cdot 3 \cdot 2 \cdot 1 = 5040$

4-17.
$8! = 8 \cdot 7 \cdot 6 \cdot 5 \cdot 4 \cdot 3 \cdot 2 \cdot 1 = 40,320$

4-19.
$5! = 5 \cdot 4 \cdot 3 \cdot 2 \cdot 1 = 120$

4-21.
$10 \cdot 10 \cdot 10 = 1000$
$1 \cdot 9 \cdot 8 = 72$

4-23.
$5 \cdot 2 = 10$

4-25.
$2^6 = 64$

4-27.
Selecting 1 coin there are 4 ways. Selecting 2 coins there are 6 ways. Selecting 3 coins there are 4 ways. Selecting 4 coins there is 1

4-27. continued
way. Hence the total is $4 + 6 + 4 + 1 = 15$ ways. (List all possibilities.)

4-29.
X = number of checkens
2X = number of chicken legs
15 − X = number of cows
4(15 − X) = number of cow legs
$2X + 4(15 − X) = 46$
$2X + 60 − 4X = 46$
$− 2X = − 14$
$X = 7$
There are 7 chickens and 8 cows.

4-31.
a. 40,320
b. 3,628,800
c. 24
d. 1
e. 1

4-32.
a. $\frac{8!}{(8-2)!} = \frac{8\cdot7\cdot6\cdot5\cdot4\cdot3\cdot2\cdot1}{6\cdot5\cdot4\cdot3\cdot2\cdot1} = 56$

b. $\frac{7!}{(7-5)!} = \frac{7\cdot6\cdot5\cdot4\cdot3\cdot2\cdot1}{2\cdot1} = 2,520$

c. $\frac{12!}{(12-4)!} = \frac{12\cdot11\cdot10\cdot9\cdot8\cdot7\cdot6\cdot5\cdot4\cdot3\cdot2\cdot1}{8\cdot7\cdot6\cdot5\cdot4\cdot3\cdot2\cdot1} = 11,880$

d. $\frac{5!}{(5-3)!} = \frac{5\cdot4\cdot3\cdot2\cdot1}{2\cdot1} = 60$

e. $\frac{6!}{(6-0)!} = \frac{6\cdot5\cdot4\cdot3\cdot2\cdot1}{6\cdot5\cdot4\cdot3\cdot2\cdot1} = 1$

f. $\frac{6!}{(6-6)!} = \frac{6\cdot5\cdot4\cdot3\cdot2\cdot1}{1} = 720$

g. $\frac{8!}{(8-0)!} = \frac{8\cdot7\cdot6\cdot5\cdot4\cdot3\cdot2\cdot1}{8\cdot7\cdot6\cdot5\cdot4\cdot3\cdot2\cdot1} = 1$

h. $\frac{8!}{(8-8)!} = \frac{8\cdot7\cdot6\cdot5\cdot4\cdot3\cdot2\cdot1}{1} = 40,320$

i. $\frac{11!}{(11-3)!} = \frac{11\cdot10\cdot9\cdot8\cdot7\cdot6\cdot5\cdot4\cdot3\cdot2\cdot1}{8\cdot7\cdot6\cdot5\cdot4\cdot3\cdot2\cdot1} = 990$

j. $\frac{6!}{(6-2)!} = \frac{6\cdot5\cdot4\cdot3\cdot2\cdot1}{4\cdot3\cdot2\cdot1} = 30$

4-33.
$_7P_4 = \frac{7!}{(7-4)!} = \frac{7\cdot6\cdot5\cdot4\cdot3\cdot2\cdot1}{3\cdot2\cdot1} = 840$

4-35.
$_{10}P_6 = \frac{10!}{(10-6)!} = \frac{10\cdot9\cdot8\cdot7\cdot6\cdot5\cdot4\cdot3\cdot2\cdot1}{4\cdot3\cdot2\cdot1} = 151,200$

4-37.
$_4P_4 = \frac{4!}{(4-4)!} = \frac{4\cdot3\cdot2\cdot1}{0!} = 24$

4-39.

$$_6P_3 = \frac{6!}{(6-3)!} = \frac{6!}{3!} = 120$$

4-41.

$$_5P_5 = \frac{5!}{(5-5)!} = \frac{5!}{0!} = 120$$

4-43.

$$_{20}P_5 = \frac{20!}{(20-5)!} = \frac{20!}{15!}$$

$$= \frac{20 \cdot 19 \cdot 18 \cdot 17 \cdot 16 \cdot 15!}{15!} = 1,860,480$$

4-45.

$$_7P_5 = \frac{7!}{(7-5)!} = \frac{7!}{2!} = \frac{7 \cdot 6 \cdot 5 \cdot 4 \cdot 3 \cdot 2!}{2!} = 2,520$$

4-46.

a. $\frac{5!}{3!\,2!} = 10$ f. $\frac{3!}{3!\,0!} = 1$

b. $\frac{8!}{5!\,3!} = 56$ g. $\frac{3!}{0!\,3!} = 1$

c. $\frac{7!}{3!\,4!} = 35$ h. $\frac{9!}{2!\,7!} = 36$

d. $\frac{6!}{4!\,2!} = 15$ i. $\frac{12!}{10!\,2!} = 66$

e. $\frac{6!}{2!\,4!} = 15$ j. $\frac{4!}{1!\,3!} = 4$

4-47.

$$_{52}C_3 = \frac{52!}{49!\,3!} = \frac{52 \cdot 51 \cdot 50 \cdot 49!}{49! \cdot 3 \cdot 2 \cdot 1} = 22,100$$

4-49.

$$_{12}C_4 \cdot {}_9C_3 = \frac{12!}{8!\,4!} \cdot \frac{9!}{6!\,3!}$$

$$= \frac{12 \cdot 11 \cdot 10 \cdot 9 \cdot 8!}{8! \cdot 4 \cdot 3 \cdot 2 \cdot 1} \cdot \frac{9 \cdot 8 \cdot 7 \cdot 6!}{6! \cdot 3 \cdot 2 \cdot 1} = 41,580$$

4-51.

$$_{10}C_3 = \frac{10!}{7!\,3!} = \frac{10 \cdot 9 \cdot 8 \cdot 7!}{7! \cdot 3 \cdot 2 \cdot 1} = 120$$

4-53.

$$_{11}C_6 = \frac{11!}{5!\,6!} = \frac{11 \cdot 10 \cdot 9 \cdot 8 \cdot 7 \cdot 6!}{6! \cdot 5 \cdot 4 \cdot 3 \cdot 2 \cdot 1} = 462$$

4-55.

$$_4C_2 \cdot {}_{12}C_5 \cdot {}_7C_3 = \frac{4!}{2!\,2!} \cdot \frac{12!}{7!\,5!} \cdot \frac{7!}{4!\,3!}$$

$$= \frac{4 \cdot 3 \cdot 2!}{2! \cdot 2 \cdot 1} \cdot \frac{12 \cdot 11 \cdot 10 \cdot 9 \cdot 8 \cdot 7!}{7! \cdot 5 \cdot 4 \cdot 3 \cdot 2 \cdot 1} \cdot \frac{7 \cdot 6 \cdot 5 \cdot 4!}{4! \cdot 3 \cdot 2 \cdot 1}$$

$$= 6 \cdot 792 \cdot 35 = 166,320$$

4-57.

$$_{10}C_3 \cdot {}_{10}C_3 = \frac{10!}{7!\,3!} \cdot \frac{10!}{7!\,3!}$$

$$= \frac{10 \cdot 9 \cdot 8 \cdot 7!}{7! \cdot 3 \cdot 2 \cdot 1} \cdot \frac{10 \cdot 9 \cdot 8 \cdot 7!}{7! \cdot 3 \cdot 2 \cdot 1} = 120 \cdot 120 = 14,400$$

4-59.

$$_{12}C_6 \cdot {}_{10}C_6 = \frac{12!}{6!\,6!} \cdot \frac{10!}{4!\,6!}$$

$$= \frac{12 \cdot 11 \cdot 10 \cdot 9 \cdot 8 \cdot 7 \cdot 6!}{6! \cdot 6 \cdot 5 \cdot 4 \cdot 3 \cdot 2 \cdot 1} \cdot \frac{10 \cdot 9 \cdot 8 \cdot 7 \cdot 6!}{6! \cdot 4 \cdot 3 \cdot 2 \cdot 1}$$

$$= 924 \cdot 210 = 194,040$$

4-61.

$$_{25}C_5 = \frac{25!}{20!\,5!} = \frac{25 \cdot 24 \cdot 23 \cdot 22 \cdot 21 \cdot 20!}{20! \cdot 5 \cdot 4 \cdot 3 \cdot 2 \cdot 1}$$

$$= 53,130$$

4-63.

$$_9C_5 = \frac{9!}{4!\,5!} = \frac{9 \cdot 8 \cdot 7 \cdot 6 \cdot 5!}{5! \cdot 4 \cdot 3 \cdot 2 \cdot 1} = 126$$

4-65.

$$_{10}C_8 = \frac{10!}{2!\,8!} = \frac{10 \cdot 9 \cdot 8!}{8! \cdot 2 \cdot 1} = 45$$

4-67.

$$_{17}C_8 = \frac{17!}{9!\,8!} = \frac{17 \cdot 16 \cdot 15 \cdot 14 \cdot 13 \cdot 12 \cdot 11 \cdot 10 \cdot 9!}{9! \cdot 8 \cdot 7 \cdot 6 \cdot 5 \cdot 4 \cdot 3 \cdot 2 \cdot 1}$$

$$= 24,310$$

4-69.

a. 4

b. $9 \cdot 4 + 4 = 40$

c. $48 \cdot 13 = 624$

d. $13 \cdot 12 \cdot {}_4C_3 \cdot {}_4C_2 = 3744$

4-71.

$$_5P_5 = \frac{5!}{(5-5)!} = \frac{5!}{0!} = 120$$

4-73.

$$13 \cdot {}_4C_2 = 13 \cdot \frac{4!}{2!\,2!} = 13 \cdot \frac{24}{2 \cdot 2} = 78$$

4-75.

$$_{12}C_5 = \frac{12!}{(12-5)!\,5!} = \frac{12 \cdot 11 \cdot 10 \cdot 9 \cdot 8 \cdot 7!}{7! \cdot 5 \cdot 4 \cdot 3 \cdot 2 \cdot 1} = 792$$

4-77.

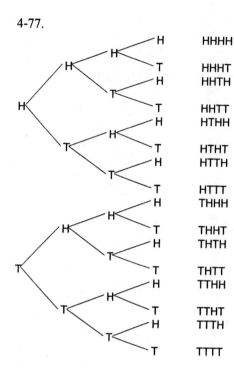

	HHHH
	HHHT
	HHTH
	HHTT
	HTHH
	HTHT
	HTTH
	HTTT
	THHH
	THHT
	THTH
	THTT
	TTHH
	TTHT
	TTTH
	TTTT

4-79.

$$8! = {}_8P_8 = \frac{8!}{(8-8)!} = \frac{8!}{0!} = 40,320$$

4-81.

$${}_6C_3 \cdot {}_5C_2 \cdot {}_4C_1 = \frac{6!}{3!\,3!} \cdot \frac{5!}{3!\,2!} \cdot \frac{4!}{3!\,1!}$$

$$= 20 \cdot 10 \cdot 4 = 800$$

4-83.

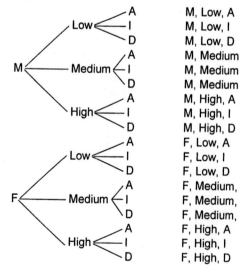

	Low	A	M, Low, A
		I	M, Low, I
		D	M, Low, D
M	Medium	A	M, Medium
		I	M, Medium
		D	M, Medium
	High	A	M, High, A
		I	M, High, I
		D	M, High, D
	Low	A	F, Low, A
		I	F, Low, I
		D	F, Low, D
F	Medium	A	F, Medium,
		I	F, Medium,
		D	F, Medium,
	High	A	F, High, A
		I	F, High, I
		D	F, High, D

4-85.

$${}_6P_6 = \frac{6!}{(6-6)!} = \frac{6!}{0!} = 6 \cdot 5 \cdot 4 \cdot 3 \cdot 2 \cdot 1 = 720$$

4-87.

$${}_4P_4 = \frac{4!}{(4-4)!} = \frac{4!}{0!} = 24$$

4-89.

$$5^2 = 25$$

$${}_5P_2 = \frac{5!}{(5-2)!} = \frac{5 \cdot 4 \cdot 3!}{3!} = 20$$

4-91.

$2 \cdot 2 = 4$, assuming the sweater cannot be worn under the blouse.

4-93.

$$5 \cdot 3 \cdot 2 = 30$$

4-95.

$${}_{12}C_4 = \frac{12!}{8!\,4!} = \frac{12 \cdot 11 \cdot 10 \cdot 9 \cdot 8!}{4 \cdot 3 \cdot 2 \cdot 1 \cdot 8!} = 495$$

4-97.

$${}_{20}C_5 = \frac{20!}{15!\,5!} = \frac{20 \cdot 19 \cdot 18 \cdot 17 \cdot 16 \cdot 15!}{15! \cdot 5 \cdot 4 \cdot 3 \cdot 2 \cdot 1} = 15,504$$

Chapter Quiz
1. False
2. False
3. True
4. True
5. False
6. b
7. d
8. d
9. b
10. b
11. tree diagram
12. 12
13. n^k
14. n!
15. permutations
16. 1,188,137,600; 710,424,000
17. 720
18. 33,554,432
19. 35

20. 8

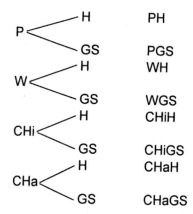

PH	
PGS	
WH	
WGS	
CHiH	
CHiGS	
CHaH	
CHaGS	

21. 2,646
22. 40,320
23.

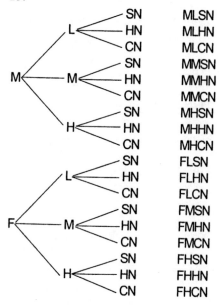

MLSN	
MLHN	
MLCN	
MMSN	
MMHN	
MMCN	
MHSN	
MHHN	
MHCN	
FLSN	
FLHN	
FLCN	
FMSN	
FMHN	
FMCN	
FHSN	
FHHN	
FHCN	

24. 1,365
25. 64; 24
26. 4 or 6 if he wears a sweater over the shirt.
27. 120
28. 5,005
29. 60
30. 15

5-1.
A probability experiment is a chance process which leads to well-defined outcomes.

5-3.
An outcome is the result of a single trial of a probability experiment, whereas an event can consist of one or more outcomes.

5-5.
The range of values is $0 \leq P(E) \leq 1$.

5-7.
0

5-9.
$1 - 0.85 = 0.15$

5-11.
a. empirical   e. empirical
b. classical   f. empirical
c. empirical   g. subjective
d. classical

5-12.
a. $\frac{1}{6}$ e. 1
b. $\frac{1}{2}$ f. $\frac{5}{6}$
c. $\frac{1}{3}$ g. $\frac{1}{6}$
d. 1

5-13.
The sample space for two dice is used. There are 36 outcomes.

a. There are 5 ways to get a sum of 6. They are (1,5), (2,4), (3,3), (4,2), and (5,1). The probability then is $\frac{5}{36}$.

b. There are six ways to get doubles. They are (1,1), (2,2), (3,3), (4,4), (5,5), and (6,6). The probability then is $\frac{6}{36} = \frac{1}{6}$.

c. There are six ways to get a sum of 7. They are (1,6), (2,5), (3,4), (4,3), (5,2), and (6,1). There are two ways to get a sum of 11. They are (5,6) and (6,5). Hence, the total number of ways to get a 7 or 11 is eight. The probability then is $\frac{8}{36} = \frac{2}{9}$.

d. To get a sum greater than nine, one must roll a 10, 11, or 12. There are six ways to get a 10, 11, or 12. They are (4,6), (5,5), (6,4), (5,6), (6,5), and (6,6). The probability then is $\frac{6}{36} = \frac{1}{6}$.

5-13. continued
e. To get a sum less than or equal to four, one must roll a 4, 3, or 2. There are six ways to do this. They are (3,1), (2,2), (1,3), (2,1), (1,2), and (1,1). The probability is $\frac{6}{36} = \frac{1}{6}$.

5-14.
a. $\frac{1}{13}$ f. $\frac{4}{13}$
b. $\frac{1}{4}$ g. $\frac{1}{2}$
c. $\frac{1}{52}$ h. $\frac{1}{26}$
d. $\frac{2}{13}$ i. $\frac{7}{13}$
e. $\frac{4}{13}$ j. $\frac{1}{26}$

5-15.
The sample space is 5 red, 2 white, and 3 green marbles.

a. $P(\text{red}) = \frac{5}{10} = \frac{1}{2}$

b. $P(\text{green}) = \frac{3}{10}$

c. $P(\text{red or white}) = \frac{5}{10} + \frac{2}{10} = \frac{7}{10}$

d. $P(\text{not green}) = 1 - P(\text{green})$

$= 1 - \frac{3}{10} = \frac{7}{10}$

e. $P(\text{not red}) = 1 - P(\text{red}) = \frac{1}{2}$

5-17.
$\frac{7}{50}$

5-19.
$1 - 0.53 = 0.47$

5-21.
The sample space is BBB, BBG, BGB, GBB, GGB, GBG, BGG, and GGG.

a. All boys is the outcome BBB; hence $P(\text{all boys}) = \frac{1}{8}$.

b. All girls or all boys would be BBB and GGG; hence, $P(\text{all girls or all boys}) = \frac{1}{4}$.

c. Exactly two boys or two girls would be BBG, BGB, GBB, BBG, GBG, or BGG. The probability then is $\frac{6}{8} = \frac{3}{4}$.

5-21. continued

d. At least one child of each gender means at least one boy or at least one girl. The outcomes are the same as those of part c, hence the probability is the same, $\frac{3}{4}$.

5-23.

The outcomes for 2, 3, or 12 are (1,1), (1,2), (2,1), and (6,6); hence P(2, 3, or 12) = $\frac{1+2+1}{36} = \frac{4}{36} = \frac{1}{9}$.

5-25.

a. There are 18 odd numbers; hence, P(odd) = $\frac{18}{36} = \frac{9}{19}$.

b. There are 11 numbers greater than 25 (26 through 36) hence, the probability is $\frac{11}{38}$.

c. There are 14 numbers less than 15 hence the probability is $\frac{14}{38} = \frac{7}{19}$.

5-27.

0.331 (53) = 17.543 $\approx$ 18

5-29.

Each die can land in six different ways, hence the total number of outcomes is $6 \cdot 6 \cdot 6 = 216$. There are six triples: (1, 1, 1), (2, 2, 2), (3, 3, 3), (4, 4, 4), (5, 5, 5), and (6, 6, 6). Hence, the probability of getting triples is $\frac{6}{216} = \frac{1}{36}$.

5-31.

a. 0.08

b. 0.01

c. $0.08 + 0.27 = 0.35$

d. $0.01 + 0.24 + 0.11 = 0.36$

5-33.

The statement is probably not based on empirical probability.

5-35.

Actual outcomes will vary, however each number should occur approximately $\frac{1}{6}$ of the time.

5-37.

a. 1:5, 5:1
b. 1:1, 1:1
c. 1:3, 3:1
d. 1:1, 1:1
e. 1:12, 12:1
f. 1:3, 3:1
g. 1:1, 1:1

5-39.

Answers will vary.

5-41.

$\frac{2}{12} = \frac{1}{6}$

5-43.

$\frac{4}{19} + \frac{7}{19} = \frac{11}{19}$

5-45.

a. $\frac{5}{17} + \frac{3}{17} = \frac{8}{17}$

b. $\frac{4}{17} + \frac{2}{17} = \frac{6}{17}$

c. $\frac{3}{17} + \frac{2}{17} + \frac{4}{17} = \frac{9}{17}$

d. $\frac{5}{17} + \frac{4}{17} + \frac{3}{17} = \frac{12}{17}$

5-47.

$0.80 + 0.55 - 0.42 = 0.93$

5-49.

	Junior	Senior	Total
Female	6	6	12
Male	12	4	16
Total	18	10	28

a. $\frac{18}{28} + \frac{12}{28} - \frac{6}{28} = \frac{24}{28} = \frac{6}{7}$

b. $\frac{10}{28} + \frac{12}{28} - \frac{6}{28} = \frac{16}{28} = \frac{4}{7}$

c. $\frac{18}{28} + \frac{10}{28} = \frac{28}{28} = 1$

5-51.

Product	Co. A	Co. B	Co. C	Total
Dresses	24	18	12	54
Blouses	13	36	15	64
Total	37	54	27	118

a. P(A or dress) = $\frac{37}{118} + \frac{54}{118} - \frac{24}{118} = \frac{67}{118}$

b. P(B or C) = $\frac{54}{118} + \frac{27}{118} = \frac{81}{118}$

c. P(blouse or A) = $\frac{64}{118} + \frac{37}{118} - \frac{13}{118} = \frac{88}{118}$

5-53.

	Cashier	Clerk	Deli	Total
Married	8	12	3	23
Not Married	5	15	2	22
Total	13	27	5	45

5-53. continued

a. P(stock clerk or married) = P(clerk) + P(married) − P(married stock clerk) = $\frac{27}{45} + \frac{23}{45} - \frac{12}{45} = \frac{38}{45}$

b. P(not married) = $\frac{22}{45}$

c. P(cashier or not married) = P(cashier) + P(not married) − P(unmarried cashier) = $\frac{13}{45} + \frac{22}{45} - \frac{5}{45} = \frac{30}{45} = \frac{2}{3}$

5-55.

	Ch. 6	Ch. 8	Ch. 10	Total
Quiz	5	2	1	8
Comedy	3	2	8	13
Drama	4	4	2	10
Total	12	8	11	31

a. P(quiz show or channel 8) = P(quiz) + P(channel 8) − P(quiz show on ch. 8) = $\frac{8}{31} + \frac{8}{31} - \frac{2}{31} = \frac{14}{31}$

b. P(drama or comedy) = P(drama) + P(comedy) = $\frac{13}{31} + \frac{10}{31} = \frac{23}{31}$

c. P(channel 10 or drama) = P(ch. 10) + P(drama) − P(drama on channel 10) = $\frac{11}{31} + \frac{10}{31} - \frac{2}{31} = \frac{19}{31}$

5-57.

The total of the frequencies is 30.

a. $\frac{2}{30} = \frac{1}{15}$

b. $\frac{2+3+5}{30} = \frac{10}{30} = \frac{1}{3}$

c. $\frac{12+8+2+3}{30} = \frac{25}{30} = \frac{5}{6}$

d. $\frac{12+8+2+3}{30} = \frac{25}{30} = \frac{5}{6}$

e. $\frac{8+2}{30} = \frac{10}{30} = \frac{1}{3}$

5-59.

The total of the frequencies is 24.

a. $\frac{10}{24} = \frac{5}{12}$

b. $\frac{2+1}{24} = \frac{3}{24} = \frac{1}{8}$

c. $\frac{10+3+2+1}{24} = \frac{16}{24} = \frac{2}{3}$

d. $\frac{8+10+3+2}{24} = \frac{23}{24}$

5-61.

a. There are 4 kings, 4 queens, and 4 jacks; hence P(king or queen or jack) = $\frac{12}{52} = \frac{3}{13}$

b. There are 13 clubs, 13 hearts, and 13 spades; hence, P(club or heart or spade) = $\frac{13+13+13}{52} = \frac{39}{52} = \frac{3}{4}$

c. There are 4 kings, 4 queens, and 13 diamonds but the king and queen of diamonds were counted twice, hence; P(king or queen or diamond) = P(king) + P(queen) + P(diamond) − P(king and queen of diamonds) = $\frac{4}{52} + \frac{4}{52} + \frac{13}{52} - \frac{2}{52} = \frac{19}{52}$

d. There are 4 aces, 13 diamonds, and 13 hearts. There is one ace of diamonds and one ace of hearts; hence, P(ace or diamond or heart) = P(ace) + P(diamond) + P(heart) − P(ace of hearts and ace of diamonds) = $\frac{4}{52} + \frac{13}{52} + \frac{13}{52} - \frac{2}{52} = \frac{28}{52} = \frac{7}{13}$

e. There are 4 nines, 4 tens, 13 spades, and 13 clubs. There is one nine of spades, one ten of spades, one nine of clubs and one ten of clubs. Hence, P(9 or 10 or spade or club) = P(9) + P(10) + P(spade) + P(club) − P(9 and 10 of clubs and spades) = $\frac{4}{52} + \frac{4}{52} + \frac{13}{52} + \frac{13}{52} - \frac{4}{52} = \frac{30}{52} = \frac{15}{26}$

5-63.

P(red or white ball) = $\frac{7}{10}$

5-65.

P(mushrooms or pepperoni) = P(mushrooms) + P(pepperoni) − P(mushrooms and pepperoni)

Let X = P(mushrooms and pepperoni)

Then 0.55 = 0.32 + 0.17 − X

X = 0.06

5-67.

P(not a two-car garage) = 1 − 0.70 = 0.30

5-69.

a. independent   e. independent
b. dependent   f. dependent
c. dependent   g. dependent
d. dependent   h. independent

5-71.

P(two with elevated blood pressure) = $(.68)^2 = 0.462$ or 46.2%

5-73.
$P(\text{4 sales}) = (0.23)^4 = 0.003$

5-75.
$P(\text{two born in the same month}) = \frac{12}{12} \cdot \frac{1}{12}$
$= \frac{1}{12}$

5-77.
$P(\text{three born in March}) = \frac{1}{1728}$

5-79.
$P(\text{all three have the same birthday}) =$
$\frac{365}{365} \cdot \frac{1}{365} \cdot \frac{1}{365} = \frac{1}{133,225}$

5-81.
$P(\text{1st good and 2nd defective}) = \frac{4}{6} \cdot \frac{2}{5} = \frac{4}{15}$

5-83.
$\frac{90}{120} \cdot \frac{89}{119} \cdot \frac{88}{118} \cdot \frac{87}{117} \cdot \frac{86}{116} = \frac{42,097}{182,546}$

5-85.
$\frac{5}{8} \cdot \frac{4}{7} \cdot \frac{3}{6} = \frac{5}{28}$

5-87.
$\frac{18}{30} \cdot \frac{17}{30} = \frac{51}{145}$

5-89.

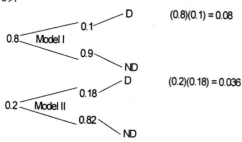

$P(\text{defective}) = 0.08 + 0.036 = 0.116$

5-91.

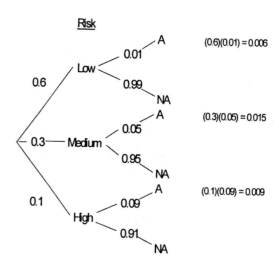

Risk

$P(\text{accident}) = .006 + .015 + .009 = 0.03$

5-93.
$P(\text{red ball}) = \frac{1}{3} \cdot \frac{4}{10} + \frac{1}{3} \cdot \frac{2}{5} + \frac{1}{3} \cdot \frac{1}{5} = \frac{1}{3}$

5-95.
$P(\text{auto will be found within one week} \mid \text{it's}$
$\text{been stolen}) = \frac{P(\text{stolen and found within 1 week})}{P(\text{stolen})}$
$= \frac{0.0009}{0.0015} = 0.6$

5-97.
$P(\text{swim} \mid \text{bridge}) = \frac{P(\text{play bridge and swim})}{P(\text{play bridge})}$

$= \frac{0.73}{0.82} = 0.89 \text{ or } 89\%$

5-99.
$P(\text{garage} \mid \text{deck}) = \frac{0.42}{0.60} = 0.7$

5-101.
$P(\text{champagne} \mid \text{bridge}) = \frac{0.68}{0.83} = 0.82$ or
82%

5-103.

	Owns	Doesn't Own	Total
Employed	18	29	47
Unemployed	28	34	62
Total	46	63	109

a. $P(\text{owns a card} \mid \text{employed}) = \frac{18}{109} \div \frac{47}{109}$
$= \frac{18}{47}$

b. $P(\text{unemployed} \mid \text{owns a card}) =$
$\frac{28}{109} \div \frac{46}{109} = \frac{14}{23}$

5-105.
P(at least one female) = 1 − P(all males)
$1 - \frac{3}{8} \cdot \frac{2}{7} \cdot \frac{1}{6} = 1 - \frac{1}{56} = \frac{55}{56}$

5-107.
P(at least one correct) = 1 − P(none
correct) =
$1 - (\frac{1}{2})^5 = 1 - \frac{1}{32} = \frac{31}{32}$

5-109.
P(at least one girl) = 1 − P(all boys)
$1 - (\frac{1}{2})^5 = 1 - \frac{1}{32} = \frac{31}{32}$

5-111.
P(at least one club) = 1 − P(no clubs)
$1 - \frac{39}{52} \cdot \frac{38}{51} \cdot \frac{37}{50} \cdot \frac{36}{49} = 1 - \frac{6327}{20,825}$
$= \frac{14,498}{20,825}$

5-113.
P(at least one defective) = 1 − P(no
defective) = $1 - (.94)^5 = 0.266$ or 26.6%

5-115.
P(at least one tail) = 1 − P(no tails)
$1 - (\frac{1}{2})^6 = 1 - \frac{1}{64} = \frac{63}{64}$

5-117.
P(at least one 6) = 1 − P(no 6's)
$1 - (\frac{5}{6})^5 = 1 - \frac{3125}{7776} = \frac{4651}{7776}$

5-119.
P(at least one even) = 1 − P(no evens)
$1 - (\frac{1}{2})^3 = 1 - \frac{1}{8} = \frac{7}{8}$

5-121.
a. $\frac{1}{6}$ b. $\frac{1}{6}$ c. $\frac{4}{6} = \frac{2}{3}$

5-123.
$\frac{16}{45}$

5-125.
$\frac{850}{1500} = \frac{17}{30}$

5-127.
a. $\frac{3}{30} = \frac{1}{10}$ c. $\frac{16+7+3}{30} = \frac{26}{30} = \frac{13}{15}$

b. $\frac{7+4}{30} = \frac{11}{30}$ d. $1 - \frac{4}{30} = \frac{26}{30} = \frac{13}{15}$

5-129.
$0.80 + 0.30 - 0.12 = 0.98$

5-131.
$(0.78)^5 = 0.289$ or 28.9%

5-133.
a. $\frac{26}{52} \cdot \frac{25}{51} \cdot \frac{24}{50} = \frac{2}{17}$

b. $\frac{13}{52} \cdot \frac{12}{51} \cdot \frac{11}{50} = \frac{33}{2550} = \frac{11}{850}$

c. $\frac{4}{52} \cdot \frac{3}{51} \cdot \frac{2}{50} = \frac{1}{5525}$

5-135.
P(C or PP) = P(C) + P(PP) = $\frac{2+3}{13} = \frac{5}{13}$

5-137.
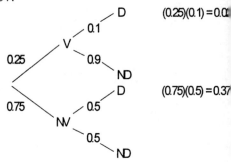

$(0.25)(0.1) = 0.0$

$(0.75)(0.5) = 0.37$

P(disease) = 0.025 + 0.375 = 0.4

5-139.
$P(NC \mid C) = \frac{P(NC \text{ and } C)}{P(C)} = \frac{0.37}{0.73} = 0.51$

5-141.
$\frac{0.43}{0.75} = 0.573$ or 57.3%

5-143.

	Low	Ave	High	Total
Graduated	6	18	43	67
Did Not Graduate	27	16	7	50
Total	33	34	50	117

a. $\frac{6}{67}$ b. $\frac{7}{50}$

5-145.
P(at least one does not wear a helmet) =
1 − P(none do not wear a helmet)
= 1 − P(all 4 wear a helmet)
= $1 - (0.23)^4 = 0.997$ or 99.7%

5-147.
P(at least one has chronic sinusitis) =
1 − P(none has chronic sinusitis)
$1 - (0.85)^5 = 0.556$ or 55.6%

Quiz

1. False, subjective probability can be used when other types of probabilities cannot be found.
2. False, empirical probability uses frequency distributions.
3. True
4. False, $P(A \text{ or } B) = P(A) + P(B) - P(A \text{ and } B)$
5. False, the probabilities can be different.
6. False, complementary events cannot occur at the same time.
7. b
8. b and d
9. d
10. b
11. c
12. sample space
13. zero, one
14. zero
15. one
16. mutually exclusive
17. a. $\frac{4}{52} = \frac{1}{13}$ c. $\frac{16}{52} = \frac{4}{13}$

 b. $\frac{4}{52} = \frac{1}{13}$

18. a. $\frac{13}{52} = \frac{1}{4}$ d. $\frac{4}{52} = \frac{1}{13}$

 b. $\frac{4+13-1}{52} = \frac{4}{13}$ e. $\frac{26}{52} = \frac{1}{2}$

 c. $\frac{1}{52}$

19. a. $\frac{12}{31}$ c. $\frac{27}{31}$

 b. $\frac{12}{31}$ d. $\frac{24}{31}$

20. a. $\frac{11}{36}$ d. $\frac{1}{3}$

 b. $\frac{5}{18}$ e. 0

 c. $\frac{11}{36}$ f. $\frac{11}{12}$

21. $(0.75 - 0.16) + (0.25 - 0.16) = 0.68$

22. $(0.3)^5 = 0.002$

23. a. $\frac{26}{52} \cdot \frac{25}{51} \cdot \frac{24}{50} \cdot \frac{23}{49} \cdot \frac{22}{48} = \frac{253}{9996}$

 b. $\frac{13}{52} \cdot \frac{12}{51} \cdot \frac{11}{50} \cdot \frac{10}{49} \cdot \frac{9}{48} = \frac{33}{66,640}$

 c. 0

24. $\frac{0.35}{0.65} = 0.54$

25. $\frac{0.16}{0.3} = 0.53$

26. $\frac{0.57}{0.7} = 0.81$

27. $\frac{0.028}{0.5} = 0.056$

28. a. $\frac{1}{2}$ b. $\frac{3}{7}$

29. $1 - (0.45)^6 = 0.99$

30. $1 - (\frac{5}{6})^4 = 0.518$

31. $1 - (0.15)^6 = 0.9999886$

6-1.
A random variable is a variable whose values are determined by chance. Examples will vary.

6-3.
The number of commercials a radio station plays during each hour.
The number of times a student uses his or her calculator during a mathematics exam.
The number of leaves on a specific type of tree.

6-5.
A probability distribution is a distribution which consists of the values a random variable can assume along with the corresponding probabilities of these values.

6-7.
Yes

6-9.
Yes

6-11.
No, probability values cannot be greater than 1.

6-13.
Discrete

6-15.
Continuous

6-17.
Discrete

6-19.

X	0	1	2	3
P(X)	$\frac{6}{15}$	$\frac{5}{15}$	$\frac{3}{15}$	$\frac{1}{15}$

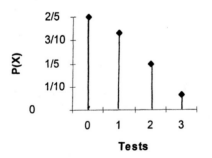

6-21.

X	0	1	2	3	4	5
P(X)	0.75	0.17	0.04	0.025	0.01	0.005

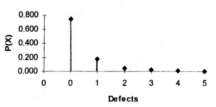

6-23.

X	1	2	3	4	5	6
P(X)	$\frac{1}{2}$	$\frac{1}{6}$	$\frac{1}{12}$	$\frac{1}{12}$	$\frac{1}{12}$	$\frac{1}{12}$

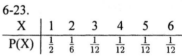

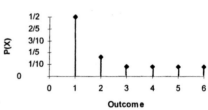

6-25.

X	1	2	3	4	5
P(X)	0.1	0.25	0.25	0.2	0.2

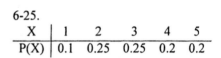

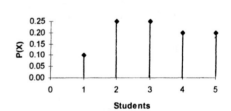

6-27.

X	$1	$5	$10	$20
P(X)	$\frac{3}{7}$	$\frac{2}{7}$	$\frac{1}{7}$	$\frac{1}{7}$

6-29.

X	1	2	3	4
P(X)	$\frac{1}{4}$	$\frac{1}{4}$	$\frac{3}{8}$	$\frac{1}{8}$

6-31.

X	1	2	3
P(X)	$\frac{1}{6}$	$\frac{1}{3}$	$\frac{1}{2}$

Yes.

6-33.

X	3	4	7
P(X)	$\frac{3}{6}$	$\frac{4}{6}$	$\frac{7}{6}$

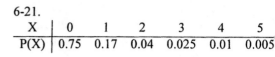
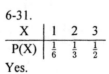

6-33. continued

No, the sum of the probabilities is greater than one and $P(7) = \frac{7}{6}$ which is also greater than one.

6-35.

X	1	2	4
P(X)	$\frac{1}{7}$	$\frac{2}{7}$	$\frac{4}{7}$

Yes.

6-37.

X	0	1	2	3
P(X)	0.92	0.03	0.03	0.02

$\mu = \sum X \cdot P(X) = 0(0.92) + 1(0.03) +$

$2(0.03) + 3(0.02) = 0.15$ or 0.2

$\sigma^2 = \sum X^2 \cdot P(X) - \mu^2 = 0^2(0.92) +$

$1^2(0.03) + 2^2(0.03) + 3^2(0.02) = 0.3075$

$\sigma = \sqrt{0.3075} = 0.55$ or 0.6

The company would need $0.2(10) = 2$ extra transistors on hand each day.

X	P(X)	$X \cdot P(X)$	$X^2 \cdot P(X)$
0	0.92	0	0
1	0.03	0.03	0.03
2	0.03	0.06	0.12
3	0.02	0.06	0.18
		$\mu = 0.15$	0.33

6-39.

$\mu = \sum X \cdot P(X) = 0(0.18) + 1(0.44) +$

$2(0.27) + 3(0.08) + 4(0.03) = 1.34$

$\sigma^2 = \sum X^2 \cdot P(X) - \mu^2 = [0^2(0.18) +$

$1^2(0.44) + 2^2(0.27) + 3^2(0.08) + 4^2(0.03)]$

$- 1.34^2 = 0.92$

$\sigma = \sqrt{0.92} = 0.96$

No, on average each person has about one credit card.

X	P(X)	$X \cdot P(X)$	$X^2 \cdot P(X)$
0	0.18	0	0
1	0.44	0.44	0.44
2	0.27	0.54	1.08
3	0.08	0.24	0.72
4	0.03	0.12	0.48
		$\mu = 1.34$	2.72

6-41.

$\mu = \sum X \cdot P(X) = 0(0.06) + 1(0.42) +$

$2(0.22) + 3(0.12) + 4(0.15) + 5(0.03)$

$= 1.97$

$\sigma^2 = \sum X^2 \cdot P(X) - \mu^2 = [0^2(0.06) +$

$1^2(0.42) + 2^2(0.22) + 3^2(0.12) + 4^2(0.15)$

$+ 5^2(0.03)] - 1.97^2 = 1.65$

$\sigma = \sqrt{1.65} = 1.28$

X	P(X)	$X \cdot P(X)$	$X^2 \cdot P(X)$
0	0.06	0.00	0.00
1	0.42	0.42	0.42
2	0.22	0.44	0.88
3	0.12	0.36	1.08
4	0.15	0.60	2.40
5	0.03	0.15	0.75
		$\mu = 1.97$	5.53

She would average $200 per week.

6-43.

$\mu = \sum X \cdot P(X) = 5(0.2) + 6(0.25) +$

$7(0.38) + 8(0.10) + 9(0.07) = 6.59$

$\sigma^2 = \sum X^2 \cdot P(X) - \mu^2 = [5^2(0.2) +$

$6^2(0.25) + 7^2(0.38) + 8^2(0.10) +$

$9^2(0.07) - 6.59^2 = 1.2619$

$\sigma = \sqrt{1.2619} = \ `1.123$

X	P(X)	$X \cdot P(X)$	$X^2 \cdot P(X)$
5	0.20	1.00	5.00
6	0.25	1.50	9.00
7	0.38	2.66	18.62
8	0.10	0.80	6.40
9	0.07	0.63	5.67
		$\mu = 6.59$	44.69

6-45.

$\mu = \sum X \cdot P(X) = 12(0.15) + 13(0.20) +$

$14(0.38) + 15(0.18) + 16(0.09) = 13.86$

$\sigma^2 = \sum X^2 \cdot P(X) - \mu^2 = [12^2(0.15) +$

$13^2(0.20) + 14^2(0.38) + 15^2(0.18) +$

$16^2(0.09)] - 13.86^2 = 1.3204$

$\sigma = \sqrt{1.3204} = 1.1491$

6-45. continued

X	P(X)	$X \cdot P(X)$	$X^2 \cdot P(X)$
12	0.15	1.80	21.60
13	0.20	2.60	33.80
14	0.38	5.32	74.48
15	0.18	2.70	40.50
16	0.09	1.44	23.04
		$\mu = 13.86$	193.42

6-47.

$E(X) = \sum X \cdot P(X) = \$4995(\frac{1}{2500}) -$
$\$5(\frac{2499}{2500}) = -\$3$

Alternate Solution:

$\$5000(\frac{1}{2500}) - \$5 = -\$3$

Yes, they will make \$7500.

6-49.

$E(X) = \sum X \cdot P(X) = \$5.00(\frac{1}{6}) = \$0.83$
He should pay about \$0.83.

6-51.

$E(X) = \sum X \cdot P(X) = \$1000(\frac{1}{1000}) +$
$\$500(\frac{1}{1000}) + \$100(\frac{5}{1000}) - \$3.00$
$= -\$1.00$

Alternate Solution:

$E(X) = 997(\frac{1}{1000}) + 497(\frac{1}{1000}) + 97(\frac{5}{1000})$
$- 3(\frac{993}{1000}) = -\$1.00$

6-53.

$E(X) = \sum X \cdot P(X) = \$500(\frac{1}{1000}) - \$1.00$
$= -\$0.50$

Alternate Solution:

$E(X) = 499(\frac{1}{1000}) - 1(\frac{999}{1000}) = -\$0.50$

There are 6 possibilities when a number with
all different digits is boxed, $(3 \cdot 2 \cdot 1 = 6)$.
Hence,
$\$80.00 \cdot \frac{6}{1000} - \$1.00 = \$0.48 - \$1.00$
$= -\$0.52$

Alternate Solution:

$E(X) = 79(\frac{6}{1000}) - 1(\frac{994}{1000}) = -\$0.52$

6-55.
The probabilities of each are:
Red: $\frac{18}{38}$ Black: $\frac{18}{38}$

1 − 18: $\frac{18}{38}$ 19 − 36: $\frac{18}{38}$

6-55. continued

0: $\frac{1}{38}$ 00: $\frac{1}{38}$

Any single number: $\frac{1}{38}$

0 or 00: $\frac{2}{38}$

$E(X) = \sum X \cdot P(X)$

a. $\$1.00(\frac{18}{38}) - \$1.00(\frac{20}{38}) = -\$0.053$

b. $\$1.00(\frac{18}{38}) - \$1.00(\frac{20}{38}) = -\$0.053$

c. $\$35(\frac{1}{38}) - \$1.00(\frac{37}{38}) = -\$0.053$

d. $\$35(\frac{1}{38}) - \$1.00(\frac{37}{38}) = -\$0.053$

e. $\$17(\frac{2}{38}) - \$1.00(\frac{36}{38}) = -\$0.053$

6-57.
The expected value for a single die is 3.5,
and since 3 die are rolled, the expected value
is $3(3.5) = 10.5$

6-59.
Answers will vary.

6-61.
Answers will vary.

6-63.
a. Yes
b. Yes
c. Yes
d. No, there are more than two outcomes.
e. No
f. Yes
g. Yes
h. Yes
i. No, there are more than two outcomes.

6-64.

a. 0.420	f. 0.250
b. 0.346	g. 0.418
c. 0.590	h. 0.176
d. 0.251	i. 0.246
e. 0.000	

6-65.
a. $P(X) = \frac{n!}{(n-X)! \, X!} \cdot p^X \cdot q^{n-X}$

$P(X) = \frac{6!}{3! \cdot 3!} \cdot (0.03)^3 (0.97)^3 = 0.000$

6-65. continued

b. $P(X) = \frac{4!}{2! \cdot 2!} \cdot (0.18)^2 \cdot (0.82)^2 = 0.131$

c. $P(X) = \frac{5!}{2! \cdot 3!} = (0.63)^3 \cdot (0.37)^2 = 0.342$

d. $P(X) = \frac{9!}{9! \cdot 0!} \cdot (0.42)^0 \cdot (0.58)^9 = 0.007$

e. $P(X) = \frac{10!}{5! \cdot 5!} \cdot (0.37)^5 \cdot (0.63)^5 = 0.173$

6-67.

$n = 10$, $p = 0.5$, $X = 6, 7, 8, 9, 10$
$P(X) = 0.205 + 0.117 + 0.044 + 0.010 + 0.001 = 0.377$
No, because the probability would be less than 50%.

6-69.

$n = 9$, $p = 0.30$, $X = 3$
$P(X) = 0.267$

6-71.

$n = 7$, $p = 0.75$, $X = 0, 1, 2, 3$
$P(X) = \frac{7!}{7! \, 0!}(0.75)^0(0.25)^7 +$

$\frac{7!}{6! \, 1!}(0.75)^1(0.25)^6 + \frac{7!}{5! \, 2!}(0.75)^2(0.25)^5 +$

$\frac{7!}{4! \, 3!}(0.75)^3(0.25)^4 = 0.071$

6-73.

$n = 5$, $p = 0.40$
a. $X = 2$, $P(X) = 0.346$
b. $X = 0, 1, 2,$ or 3 people
$P(X) = 0.078 + 0.259 + 0.346 + 0.230$
$= 0.913$
c. $X = 2, 3, 4,$ or 5 people
$P(X) = 0.346 + 0.230 + 0.077 + 0.01$
$= 0.663$
d. $X = 0, 1,$ or 2 people
$P(X) = 0.683$

6-75.

a. $n = 10$, $p = 0.2$, $X = 0, 1, 2, 3$
$P(X) = 0.107 + 0.268 + 0.302 + 0.201$
$= 0.878$
b. $n = 10$, $p = 0.2$, $X = 3$, $P(X) = 0.201$
c. $n = 10$, $p = 0.2$, $X = 5, 6, 7, 8, 9, 10$
$P(X) = 0.026 + 0.006 + 0.001 + 0 + 0 + 0$
$= 0.033$

6-76.

a. $\mu = 100(0.75) = 75$
$\sigma^2 = 100(0.75)(0.25) = 18.75$
$\sigma = \sqrt{18.75} = 4.33$

6-76. continued

b. $\mu = 300(0.3) = 90$
$\sigma^2 = 300(0.3)(0.7) = 63$
$\sigma = \sqrt{63} = 7.94$
c. $\mu = 20(0.5) = 10$
$\sigma^2 = 20(0.5)(0.5) = 5$
$\sigma = \sqrt{5} = 2.236$
d. $\mu = 10(0.8) = 8$
$\sigma^2 = 10(0.8)(0.2) = 1.6$
$\sigma = \sqrt{1.6} = 1.265$
e. $\mu = 1000(0.1) = 100$
$\sigma^2 = 1000(0.1)(0.9) = 90$
$\sigma = \sqrt{90} = 9.49$
f. $\mu = 500(0.25) = 125$
$\sigma^2 = 500(0.25)(0.75) = 93.75$
$\sigma = \sqrt{93.75} = 9.68$
g. $\mu = 50(\frac{2}{5}) = 20$
$\sigma^2 = 50(\frac{2}{5})(\frac{3}{5}) = 12$
$\sigma = \sqrt{12} = 3.464$
h. $\mu = 36(\frac{1}{6}) = 6$
$\sigma^2 = 36(\frac{1}{6})(\frac{5}{6}) = 5$
$\sigma = \sqrt{5} = 2.236$

6-77.

$n = 800$, $p = 0.01$
$\mu = 800(0.01) = 8$
$\sigma^2 = 800(0.01)(0.99) = 7.9$
$\sigma = \sqrt{7.92} = 2.8$

6-79.

$n = 500$, $p = 0.02$
$\mu = 500(0.02) = 10$
$\sigma^2 = 500(0.02)(0.98) = 9.8$
$\sigma = \sqrt{9.8} = 3.1$

6-81.

$n = 1000$, $p = 0.21$
$\mu = 1000(0.21) = 210$
$\sigma^2 = 1000(0.21)(0.79) = 165.9$
$\sigma = \sqrt{165.9} = 12.9$

6-83.

$n = 18$, $p = 0.25$, $X = 5$
$P(X) = \frac{18!}{13! \, 5!}(0.25)^5(0.75)^{13} = 0.199$

6-85.

$n = 10$, $p = \frac{1}{3}$, $X = 0, 1, 2, 3$
$P(X) = \frac{10!}{10! \, 0!}(\frac{1}{3})^0(\frac{2}{3})^{10} + \frac{10!}{9! \, 1!}(\frac{1}{3})^1(\frac{2}{3})^9$
$+ \frac{10!}{8! \, 2!}(\frac{1}{3})^2(\frac{2}{3})^8 + \frac{10!}{7! \, 3!}(\frac{1}{3})^3(\frac{2}{3})^7 = 0.559$

6-87.

$n = 5$, $p = 0.13$, $X = 3, 4, 5$

6-87. continued

$P(X) = \frac{5!}{2!\,3!}(0.13)^3(0.87)^2 +$

$\frac{5!}{1!\,4!}(0.13)^4(0.87)^1 + \frac{5!}{0!\,5!}(0.13)^5(0.87)^0$

$= 0.017$

6-89.

n = 12, p = 0.86, X = 10, 11, 12

$P(X) = \frac{12!}{2!\,10!}(0.86)^{10}(0.14)^2 +$

$\frac{12!}{1!\,11!}(0.86)^{11}(0.14)^1 + \frac{12!}{0!\,12!}(0.86)^{12}(0.14)^0$

$= 0.77$

Yes. The probability is high, 77%.

6-91.

n = 5, p = 0.2, X = 0, 1, 2, 3, 4, 5

X	0	1	2	3	4	5
P(X)	0.328	0.410	0.205	0.051	0.006	0

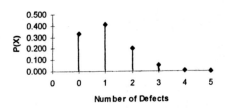

6-93.

No, the sum of the probabilities is greater than one.

6-95.

No, the sum of the probabilities is greater than one.

6-97.

X	0	1	2	3	4
P(X)	0.05	0.30	0.45	0.12	0.08

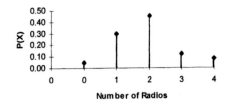

6-99.

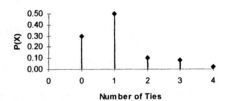

6-101.

$\mu = \sum X \cdot P(X) = 8(0.15) + 9(0.25) +$
$10(0.29) + 11(0.19) + 12(0.12) = 9.88$

$\sigma^2 = \sum X^2 \cdot P(X) - \mu^2 = [8^2(0.15) +$
$9^2(0.25) + 10^2(0.29) + 11^2(0.19) +$
$12^2(0.12)] - 9.88^2 = 1.5056$

$\sigma = \sqrt{1.5056} = 1.23$

X	P(X)	$X \cdot P(X)$	$X^2 \cdot P(X)$
8	0.15	1.20	9.60
9	0.25	2.25	20.25
10	0.29	2.90	29.00
11	0.19	2.09	22.99
12	0.12	1.44	17.28
	$\mu =$	9.88	99.12

6-103.

$\mu = \sum X \cdot P(X) = 22(0.08) + 23(0.19) +$
$24(0.36) + 25(0.25) + 26(0.07) + 27(0.05)$
$= 24.19$

$\sigma^2 = \sum X^2 \cdot P(X) - \mu^2 = [22^2(0.08) +$
$23^2(0.19) + 24^2(0.36) + 25^2(0.25) +$
$26^2(0.07) + 27^2(0.05)] - 24.19^2 = 1.4539$

$\sigma = \sqrt{1.4539} = 1.206$

X	P(X)	$X \cdot P(X)$	$X^2 \cdot P(X)$
22	0.08	1.76	38.72
23	0.19	4.37	100.51
24	0.36	8.64	207.36
25	0.25	6.25	156.25
26	0.07	1.82	47.32
27	0.05	1.35	36.45
	$\mu =$	24.19	586.61

6-105.

$\mu = \sum X \cdot P(X)$
$= \frac{1}{2}(\$1.00) + \frac{18}{52}(\$5.00) + \frac{6}{52}(\$10.00) +$
$\frac{2}{52}(\$100.00) = \$7.23$

6-105. continued
To break even, a person should bet $7.23.

6-107.
a. 0.122
b. $1 - 0.002 + 0.009 = 0.989$
c. $0.002 + 0.009 + 0.032 = 0.043$

6-109.
$\mu = n \cdot p = 180(0.75) = 135$
$\sigma^2 = n \cdot p \cdot q = 180(0.75)(0.25) = 33.75$
$\sigma = \sqrt{33.75} = 5.809$

6-111.
$n = 8, p = 0.25$
$P(X \leq 3) = \frac{8!}{8!\,0!}(0.25)^0(0.75)^8 +$
$\frac{8!}{7!\,1!}(0.25)^1(0.75)^7 + \frac{8!}{6!\,2!}(0.25)^2(0.75)^6 +$
$\frac{8!}{5!\,3!}(0.25)^3(0.75)^5 = 0.8862$

6-113.
$n = 20, p = 0.75, X = 16$
P(16 have eaten pizza for breakfast) =

$\frac{20!}{4!\,16!}(0.75)^{16}(0.25)^4 = 0.1897$

Quiz
1. True
2. False, it is a discrete random variable.
3. False, the outcomes must be independent.
4. True
5. chance
6. $\mu = n \cdot p$
7. one
8. c
9. c
10. c.
11. No, the sum of the probabilities is greater than one.
12. Yes
13. Yes
14. Yes
15.

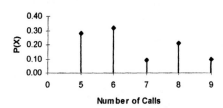

16.

X	0	1	2	3	4
P(X)	0.02	0.30	0.48	0.13	0.07

16. continued

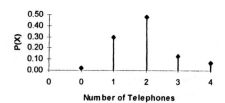

17.
$\mu = 0(0.10) + 1(0.23) + 2(0.31) + 3(0.27)$
$+ 4(0.09) = 2.02$
$\sigma^2 = [0^2(0.10) + 1^2(0.23) + 2^2(0.31) +$
$3^2(0.27) + 4^2(0.09)] - 2.02^2 = 1.3$
$\sigma = \sqrt{1.3} = 1.1$

18.
$\mu = 30(0.05) + 31(0.21) + 32(0.38) +$
$33(0.25) + 34(0.11) = 12.1$
$\sigma^2 = [30^2(0.05) + 31^2(0.21) + 32^2(0.38) +$
$33^2(0.25) + 34^2(0.11)] - 12.1^2 = 1.3$
$\sigma = \sqrt{1.3} = 1.1$

19.
$\mu = 4(\frac{1}{6}) + 5(\frac{1}{6}) + 2(\frac{1}{6}) + 10(\frac{1}{6}) + 3(\frac{1}{6})$
$+ 7(\frac{1}{6}) = 5.1$

20.
$\mu = \$2(\frac{1}{2}) + \$10(\frac{5}{26}) + \$25(\frac{3}{26}) +$
$\$100(\frac{1}{26}) = \$9.65$

21.
$n = 20, p = 0.40, X = 5$
$P(5) = 0.124$

22.
$n = 20, p = 0.60$
a. $P(15) = 0.075$
b. $P(10, 11, ..., 20) = 0.117$
c. $P(0, 1, 2, 3, 4, 5) = 0.125$

23.
$n = 300, p = 0.80$
$\mu = 300(0.80) = 240$
$\sigma^2 = 300(0.80)(0.20) = 48$
$\sigma = \sqrt{48} = 6.9$

24.
$n = 75, p = 0.12$
$\mu = 75(0.12) = 9$
$\sigma^2 = 75(0.12)(0.88) = 7.9$
$\sigma = \sqrt{7.9} = 2.8$

Note to instructors: Graphs are not to scale and are intended to convey a general idea.

7-1.
The characteristics of the normal distribution are:
1. It is bell-shaped.
2. It is symmetric about the mean.
3. The mean, median, and mode are equal.
4. It is continuous.
5. It never touches the X-axis.
6. The area under the curve is equal to one.
7. It is unimodal.

7-3.
One or 100%.

7-5.
68%, 95%, 99.7%

7-7.
The area is found by looking up z = 0.56 in Table E as shown in Block 1 of Procedure Table 6.

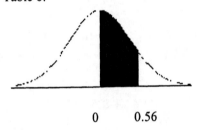

0   0.56

7-9.
The area is found by looking up z = 2.07 in Table E as shown in Block 1 of Procedure Table 6.

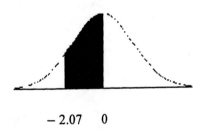

− 2.07   0

7-11.
The area is found by looking up z = 0.23 in Table E and subtracting it from 0.5 as shown in Block 2 of Procedure Table 6.
0.5 − 0.0910 = 0.4090

7-11. continued

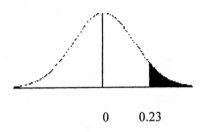

0   0.23

7-13.
The area is found by looking up z = 1.43 in Table E and subtracting it from 0.5 as shown in Block 2 of Procedure Table 6.
0.5 − 0.4236 = 0.0764

− 1.43   0

7-15.
The area is found by looking up the values 0.79 and 1.28 in Table E and subtracting the areas as shown in Block 3 of Procedure Table 6.   0.3997 − 0.2852 = 0.1145

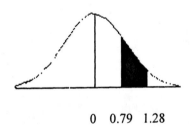

0   0.79   1.28

7-17.
The area is found by looking up the values 1.56 and 1.83 in Table E and subtracting the areas as shown in Block 3 of Procedure Table 6.   0.4664 − 0.4406 = 0.0258

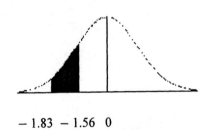

− 1.83 − 1.56 0

7-19.
The area is found by looking up the values 2.47 and 1.03 in Table E and adding them together as shown in Block 4 of Procedure Table 6. $0.3485 + 0.4932 = 0.8417$

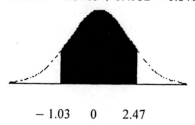

$$-1.03 \quad 0 \quad 2.47$$

7-21.
The area is found by looking up $z = 2.11$ in Table E, then adding the area to 0.5 as shown in Block 5 of Procedure Table 6.
$0.5 + 0.4826 = 0.9826$

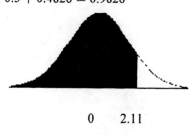

$$0 \quad 2.11$$

7-23.
The area is found by looking up $z = 0.18$ in Table E and adding it to 0.5 as shown in Block 6 of Procedure Table 6.
$0.5 + 0.0714 = 0.5714$

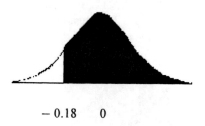

$$-0.18 \quad 0$$

7-25.
The area is found by looking up the values 1.92 and -0.44 in Table E, subtracting both areas from 0.5, and adding them together as shown in Block 7 of Procedure Table 6.
$0.5 - 0.4726 = 0.0274$
$0.5 - 0.1700 = 0.3300$
$0.0274 + 0.3300 = 0.3574$

7-25. continued

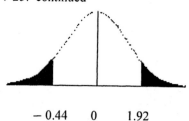

$$-0.44 \quad 0 \quad 1.92$$

7-27.
The area is found by looking up $z = 0.67$ in Table E as shown in Block 1 of Procedure Table 6.

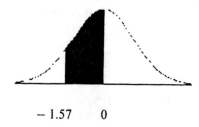

$$0 \quad 0.67$$

7-29.
The area is found by looking up $z = 1.57$ in Table E as shown in Block 1 of Procedure Table 6.
0.4418

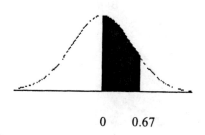

$$-1.57 \quad 0$$

7-31.
The area is found by looking up $z = 2.83$ in Table E then subtracting the area from 0.5 as shown in Block 2 of Procedure Table 6.
$0.5 - 0.4977 = 0.0023$

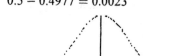
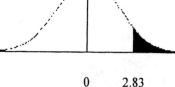

$$0 \quad 2.83$$

7-33.
The area is found by looking up $z = 1.51$ in Table E then subtracting the area from 0.5 as shown in Block 2 of Procedure Table 6.

7-33. continued
$0.5 - 0.4345 = 0.0655$

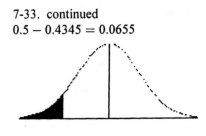

$-1.51 \qquad 0$

7-35.
The area is found by looking the values 2.46 and 1.74 in Table E and adding the areas together as shown in Block 4 of Procedure Table 6. $0.4931 + 0.4591 = 0.9522$

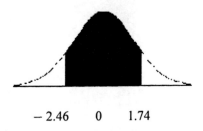

$-2.46 \qquad 0 \qquad 1.74$

7-37.
The area is found by looking up the values 1.46 and 2.97 in Table E and subtracting the areas as shown in Block 3 of Procedure Table 6. $0.4985 - 0.4279 = 0.0706$

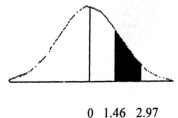

$0 \quad 1.46 \quad 2.97$

7-39.
The area is found by looking up $z = 1.42$ in Table E and adding 0.5 to it as shown in Block 5 of Procedure Table 6.
$0.5 + 0.4222 = 0.9222$

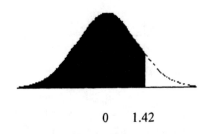

$0 \qquad 1.42$

7-41.
$z = -1.94$, found by looking up the area 0.4738 in Table E to get 1.94; it is negative because the z value is on the left side of 0.

7-43.
$z = -2.13$, found by subtracting 0.0166 from 0.5 to get 0.4834 then looking up the area to get $z = 2.13$; it is negative because the z value is on the left side of 0.

7-45.
$z = -1.26$, found by subtracting 0.5 from 0.8962 to get 0.3962, then looking up the area in Table E to get $z = 1.26$; it is negative because the z value is on the left side of 0.

7-47.
a. $z = -2.28$, found by subtracting 0.5 from 0.9886 to get 0.4886. Find the area in Table E, then find z. It is negative since the z value falls to the left of 0.

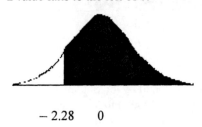

$-2.28 \qquad 0$

b. $z = -0.92$, found by subtracting 0.5 from 0.8212 to get 0.3212. Find the area in Table E, then find z. It is negative since the z value falls to the left of 0.

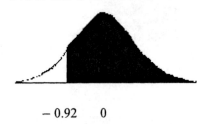

$-0.92 \qquad 0$

c. $z = -0.27$, found by subtracting 0.5 from 0.6064 to get 0.1064. Find the area in Table E, then find z. It is negative since the z value falls to the left of 0.

7-47. continued

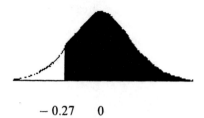

$-0.27 \quad 0$

7-49.

a. $z = \pm 1.96$, found by:

$0.05 \div 2 = 0.025$ is the area in each tail.

$0.5 - 0.025 = 0.4750$ is the area needed to determine z.

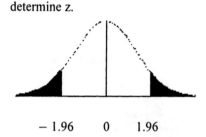

$-1.96 \quad 0 \quad 1.96$

b. $z = \pm 1.65$, found by:

$0.10 \div 2 = 0.05$ is the area in each tail.

$0.5 - 0.05 = 0.4500$ is the area needed to determine z.

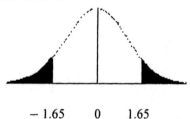

$-1.65 \quad 0 \quad 1.65$

c. $z = \pm 2.58$, found by:

$0.01 \div 2 = 0.005$ is the area in each tail.

$0.5 - 0.005 = 0.4950$ is the area needed to determine z.

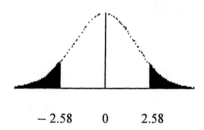

$-2.58 \quad 0 \quad 2.58$

7-51.

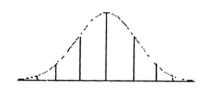

55　70　85　100　115　130　145

7-53.

Each x value $(-2, -1.5$, etc.) is substituted in the formula $y = \dfrac{e^{\frac{-x^2}{2}}}{\sqrt{2\pi}}$ to get the corresponding y value. The pairs are then plotted as shown below.

For $x = -2$, $y = \dfrac{e^{\frac{-(-2)^2}{2}}}{\sqrt{2\pi}} = \dfrac{e^{-2}}{\sqrt{6.28}}$

$= \dfrac{0.1353}{\sqrt{6.28}} = 0.05$

X	Y
-2.0	0.05
-1.5	0.13
-1.0	0.24
-0.5	0.35
0	0.40
0.5	0.35
1.0	0.24
1.5	0.13
2.0	0.05

7-55.

a. $z = \dfrac{X-\mu}{\sigma} = \dfrac{\$12.55-\$11.76}{\$2.72} = 0.29$

area $= 0.1141$

$P(z > 0.29) = 0.5 - 0.1141 = 0.3859$ or 38.59%

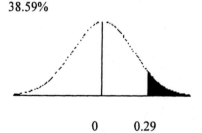

$0 \quad 0.29$

47

7-55. continued

b. $z = \frac{\$8.00 - \$11.76}{\$2.72} = -1.38$

area $= 0.4162$

$P(z < -1.38) = 0.5 - 0.4162 = 0.0838$ or 8.38%

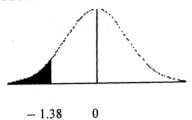

$-1.38 \qquad 0$

7-57.

$z = \frac{X - \mu}{\sigma}$

a. $z = \frac{\$35,000 - \$31,256}{\$3000} = 1.25$

area $= 0.3944$

$P(z > 1.25) = 0.5 - 0.3944 = 0.1056$ or 10.56%

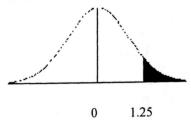

$0 \qquad 1.25$

b. $z = \frac{\$25,000 - \$31,256}{\$3000} = -2.09$

area $= 0.4817$

$P(z < -2.09) = 0.5 - 0.4817 = 0.0183$ or 1.83%

$-2.09 \qquad 0$

7-59.

a. $z = \frac{X - \mu}{\sigma} = \frac{2.5 - 4.8}{0.89} = -2.58$

area $= 0.4951$

$P(z < -2.58) = 0.5 - 0.4951 = 0.0049$ or 0.49%

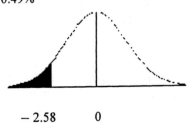

$-2.58 \qquad 0$

7-59. continued

b. $z = \frac{3 - 4.8}{0.89} = -2.02 \qquad$ area $= 0.4783$

$z = \frac{4 - 4.8}{0.89} = -0.90 \qquad$ area $= 0.3159$

$P(-2.02 < z < -0.90) = 0.4783 - 0.3159 = 0.1624$ or 16.24%

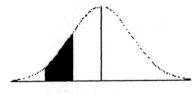

$-2.02 \quad -0.90 \qquad 0$

c. $z = \frac{4.2 - 4.8}{0.89} = -0.67 \qquad$ area $= 0.2486$

$P(z > -0.67) = 0.5 + 0.2486 = 0.7486$ or 74.86%

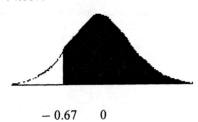

$-0.67 \qquad 0$

7-61.

a. $z = \frac{25,000 - 30,000}{2000} = -2.5$

area $= 0.4938$

$z = \frac{28,000 - 30,000}{2000} = -1.00 \qquad$ area $= 0.3413$

$P(-1 < z < -2.5) = 0.4938 - 0.3414 = 0.1525$ or 15.25%

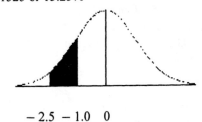

$-2.5 \quad -1.0 \quad 0$

b. $z = \frac{27,000 - 30,000}{2000} = -1.50 \quad$ area $= 0.4332$

$z = \frac{32,000 - 30,000}{2000} = 1.00 \qquad$ area $= 0.3413$

$P(-1.5 < z < 1) = 0.4332 + 0.3413 = 0.7745$ or 77.45%

7-61. continued

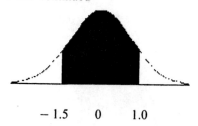

$$-1.5 \qquad 0 \qquad 1.0$$

c. $z = \frac{31,500-30,000}{2000} = 0.75$ area $= 0.2734$

$z = \frac{33,500-30,000}{2000} = 1.75$ area $= 0.4599$

$P(0.75 < z < 1.75) = 0.4599 - 0.2734$
$= 0.1865$ or 18.65%

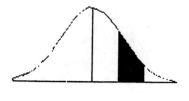

$$0 \quad 0.75 \ 1.75$$

7-63.
a. $z = \frac{180-200}{10} = -2.00$ area $= 0.4772$

$P(z \geq -2) = 0.5 + 0.4772 = 0.9772$ or
97.72%

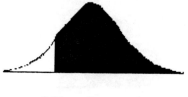

$$-2.00 \qquad 0$$

b. $z = \frac{205-200}{10} = 0.5$
area $= 0.1915$
$P(z \leq 0.5) = 0.5 + 0.1915 = 0.6915$ or
69.15%

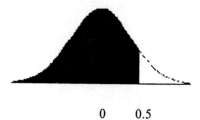

$$0 \qquad 0.5$$

7-65.
a. $z = \frac{5-9.2}{2.6} = -1.62$ area $= 0.4474$

7-65. continued
$z = \frac{10-9.2}{2.6} = 0.31$
area $= 0.1217$

$P(-1.62 < z < 0.31) = 0.4474 + 0.1217$
$= 0.5691$ or 56.91%

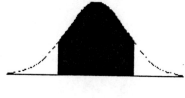

$$-1.62 \qquad 0 \qquad 0.31$$

b. $z = \frac{9-9.2}{2.6} = -0.08$ area $= 0.0319$

$z = \frac{6-9.2}{2.6} = -1.23$ area $= 0.3907$

$P(z < -1.23 \text{ or } z \geq -0.08) =$
$(0.5 - 0.33907) + (0.5 + 0.0319) =$
$0.1093 + 0.0.5319 = 0.6412$ or 64.12%

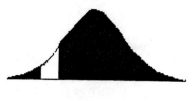

$$-1.23 \quad \uparrow \quad 0$$
$$-0.08$$

7-67.
a. $z = \frac{280-300}{8} = -2.5$ area $= 0.4938$

$P(z > -2.5) = 0.5 + 0.4938 = 0.9938$ or
99.38%

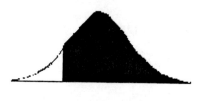

$$-2.5 \qquad 0$$

b. $z = \frac{293-300}{8} = -0.88$ area $= 0.3106$

$P(z < -0.88) = 0.5 - 0.3106 = 0.1894$ or
18.94%

7-67. continued

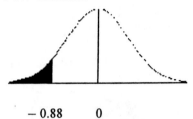

−0.88   0

c. $z = \frac{285-300}{8} = -1.88$ area = 0.4699

$z = \frac{320-300}{8} = 2.5$
area = 0.4938

$P(-1.88 < z < 2.5) = 0.4699 + 0.4938 = 0.9637$ or 96.37%

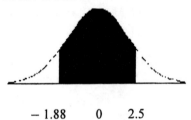

−1.88   0   2.5

7-69.
a. $z = \frac{130-132}{8} = -0.25$ area = 0.0987

$P(z > -0.25) = 0.5 + 0.0987 = 0.5987$ or 59.87%

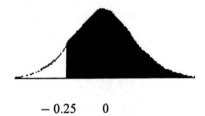

−0.25   0

b. $z = \frac{140-132}{8} = 1.00$
area = 0.3413
$P(z < 1) = 0.5 + 0.3413 = 0.8413$ or 84.13%

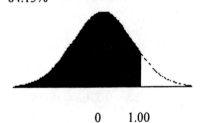

0   1.00

c. $z = \frac{131-132}{8} = -0.13$ area = 0.0517
$z = \frac{136-132}{8} = 0.50$
area = 0.1915

7-69. continued
$P(-0.13 < z < 0.50) = 0.0517 + 0.1915$
$= 0.2432$ or 24.32%

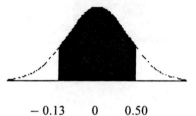

−0.13   0   0.50

7-71.
The top 75% (area) includes all but the left 25% of the curve. The corresponding z score is −0.67.
$X = -0.67(15) + 100 = 89.95$ points

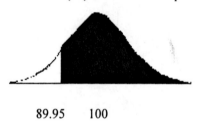

89.95   100

7-73.
The middle 80% means that 40% of the area will be on either side of the mean. The corresponding z scores will be ±1.28.
$X = -1.28(92) + 1810 = 1694.24$ sq. ft.
$X = 1.28(92) + 1810 = 1927.76$ sq. ft.

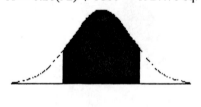

1694   1810   1928

7-75.
The "fastest" 20% (area) is in the left tail of the normal curve. The corresponding z score is found using area = 0.5 − 0.2 = 0.3. Thus z = −0.84.
$X = -0.84(4.3) + 58.6 = 54.988$
The racers should have a time of 54.988 minutes or less.

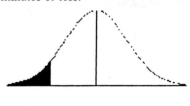

54.988   58.6

7-77.
The middle 60% means that 30% of the area
will be on either side of the mean. The
corresponding z scores will be ± 0.84.
$X = -0.84(1150) + 8256 = \$7290$
$X = 0.84(1150) + 8256 = \$9222$

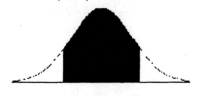

$\$7290 \quad \$8256 \quad \$9222$

7-79.
The top 12% means that 38% of the area
will be between 0 and z. The corresponding
z score will be 1.18.
$X = 1.18(16) + 57.3 = 76.18$ points

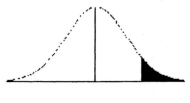

$57.3 \qquad 76.18$

7-81.
The bottom 18% means that 32% of the area
is between 0 and $-z$. The corresponding z
score will be -0.92.
$X = -0.92(6256) + 24,596 = \$18,840.48$

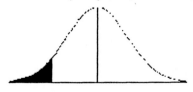

$\$18,840.48 \qquad \$24,596$

7-83.
The 10% to be exchanged would be at the
left, or bottom, of the curve; therefore, 40%
of the area is between 0 and $-z$. The
corresponding z score will be -1.28.
$X = -1.28(5) + 25 = 18.6$ months.

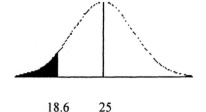

$18.6 \qquad 25$

7-85.
a. $\mu = 120 \qquad \sigma = 20$
b. $\mu = 15 \qquad \sigma = 2.5$
c. $\mu = 30 \qquad \sigma = 5$

7-87.
There are several mathematical tests that can
be used.

7-89.
2.68% area in the right tail of the curve
means that 47.32% of the area is between 0
and z, corresponding to a z score of 1.93.
$z = \frac{X-\mu}{\sigma}$
$1.93 = \frac{105-100}{\sigma}$
$1.93\sigma = 5$
$\sigma = 2.59$

7-91.
1.25% of the area in each tail means that
48.75% of the area is between 0 and $\pm z$.
The corresponding z scores are ± 2.24.
Then $\mu = \frac{42+48}{2} = 45$ and $X = \mu + z\sigma$.
$48 = 45 + 2.24\sigma$
$\sigma = 1.34$

7-93.
The distribution is called the sampling
distribution of sample means.

7-95.
The mean of the sample means is equal to
the population mean.

7-97.
The distribution will be approximately
normal when sample size is large.

7-99.
$z = \frac{\bar{X}-\mu}{\sigma/\sqrt{n}}$

7-101.
$z = \frac{\bar{X}-\mu}{\frac{\sigma}{\sqrt{n}}} = \frac{222-220}{\frac{16.3}{\sqrt{30}}} = 0.67$
$P(0 < z < 0.67) = 0.2486$ or 24.86%

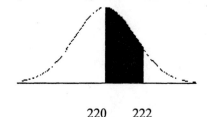

$220 \qquad 222$

7-103.

$z = \dfrac{\overline{X}-\mu}{\frac{\sigma}{\sqrt{n}}} = \dfrac{128.3-126}{\frac{15.7}{\sqrt{25}}} = 0.73$

area $= 0.2673$

$P(z > 0.73) = 0.5 - 0.2673 = 0.2327$ or 23.27%

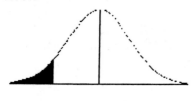

126   128.3

7-105.

$z = \dfrac{\overline{X}-\mu}{\frac{\sigma}{\sqrt{n}}} = \dfrac{\$2.00-\$2.02}{\frac{\$0.08}{\sqrt{40}}} = -1.58$

area $= 0.4429$

$P(z < -1.58) = 0.5 - 0.4429 = 0.0571$ or 5.71%

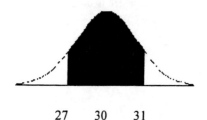

$2.00 $2.02

7-107.

$z = \dfrac{\overline{X}-\mu}{\frac{\sigma}{\sqrt{n}}} = \dfrac{27-30}{\frac{5}{\sqrt{22}}} = -2.81$

area $= 0.4975$

$z = \dfrac{\overline{X}-\mu}{\frac{\sigma}{\sqrt{n}}} = \dfrac{31-30}{\frac{5}{\sqrt{22}}} = 0.94$ area $= 0.3264$

$P(-2.81 < z < 0.94) = 0.4975 + 0.3264$
$= 0.8239$ or 82.39%

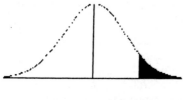

27   30   31

7-109.

$z = \dfrac{\overline{X}-\mu}{\frac{\sigma}{\sqrt{n}}} = \dfrac{44.2-43.6}{\frac{5.1}{\sqrt{50}}} = 0.83$

area $= 0.2967$

$P(z > 0.83) = 0.5 - 0.2967 = 0.2033$ or 20.33%

7-109. continued

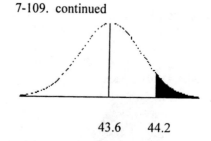

43.6   44.2

7-111.

$z = \dfrac{\overline{X}-\mu}{\frac{\sigma}{\sqrt{n}}} = \dfrac{1980-2000}{\frac{187.5}{\sqrt{50}}} = -0.75$

area $= 0.2734$

$z = \dfrac{\overline{X}-\mu}{\frac{\sigma}{\sqrt{n}}} = \dfrac{1990-2000}{\frac{187.5}{\sqrt{50}}} = -0.38$

area $= 0.1480$

$P(-0.75 < z < -0.38) = 0.2734 - 0.1480 = 0.1254$ or 12.54%

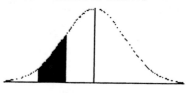

1980 1990 2000

7-113.

a. $z = \dfrac{X-\mu}{\sigma} = \dfrac{43-46.2}{8} = -0.4$

area $= 0.1554$

$P(z < -0.4) = 0.5 - 0.1554 = 0.3446$ or 34.46%

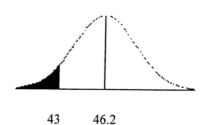

43   46.2

b. $z = \dfrac{43-46.2}{\frac{8}{\sqrt{50}}} = -2.83$ area $= 0.4977$

$P(z < -2.83) = 0.5 - 0.4977 = 0.0023$ or 0.23%

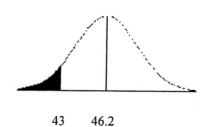

43   46.2

Chapter 7 - The Normal Distribution

7-113. continued

c. Yes, since approximately 34% will finish the exam in less than 43 minutes.

d. Very unlikely, since the probability would be less than 1%.

7-115.

a. $z = \frac{220-215}{15} = 0.33$ area = 0.1293

$P(z > 0.33) = 0.5 - 0.1293 = 0.3707$ or 37.07%

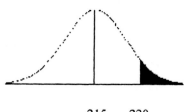

215   220

b. $z = \frac{220-215}{\frac{15}{\sqrt{25}}} = 1.67$ area = 0.4525

$P(z > 1.67) = 0.5 - 0.4525 = 0.0475$ or 4.75%

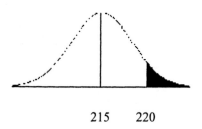

215   220

7-117.

a. $z_1 = \frac{46-48.25}{4.20} = -0.54$ area = 0.2054

$z_2 = \frac{48-48.25}{4.20} = -0.06$ area = 0.0239

$P(-0.54 < z < -0.06) = 0.2054 - 0.0239 = 0.1815$ or 18.15%

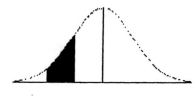

46   48   48.25

b. $z_1 = \frac{46-48.25}{\frac{4.20}{\sqrt{20}}} = -2.40$ area = 0.4918

$z_2 = \frac{48-48.25}{\frac{4.20}{\sqrt{20}}} = -0.27$ area = 0.1064

7-117. continued

$P(-2.40 < z < -0.27) = 0.4918 - 0.1064 = 0.3854$ or 38.54%

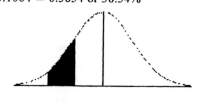

46   48   48.25

c. Means are less variable than individual data.

7-119.

Since $50 > 0.05(800)$ or 40, the correction factor is necessary.

It is $\sqrt{\frac{800-50}{800-1}} = 0.969$

$z = \frac{\bar{X}-\mu}{\frac{\sigma}{\sqrt{n}} \cdot \sqrt{\frac{N-n}{N-1}}} = \frac{83,500-82,000}{\frac{5000}{\sqrt{50}}(0.969)} = 2.19$

area = 0.4857

$P(z > 2.19) = 0.5 - 0.4857 = 0.0143$ or 1.43%

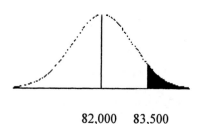

82,000   83,500

7-121.

$\sigma_x = \frac{\sigma}{\sqrt{n}} = \frac{15}{\sqrt{100}} = 1.5$

$2(1.5) = \frac{15}{\sqrt{n}}$

$3 \cdot \sqrt{n} = 15$

$\sqrt{n} = 5$

n = 25, the sample size necessary to double the standard error.

7-123.

When p is approximately 0.5, and as *n* increases, the shape of the binomial distribution becomes similar to the normal distribution. The normal approximation should be used only when $n \cdot p$ and $n \cdot q$ are both greater than or equal to 5. The correction for continuity is necessary

7-123. continued
because the normal distribution is
continuous and the binomial is discrete.

7-124.
For each problem use the following
formulas:

$$\mu = np \quad \sigma = \sqrt{npq} \quad z = \frac{X - \mu}{\sigma}$$

Be sure to correct each X for continuity.

a. $\mu = 0.5(30) = 15$
$\sigma = \sqrt{(0.5)(0.5)(30)} = 2.74$

$z = \frac{17.5 - 15}{2.74} = 0.91$ area = 0.3186

$z = \frac{18.5 - 15}{2.74} = 1.28$ area = 0.3997

$P(17.5 < X < 18.5) = 0.3997 - 0.3186$
$= 0.0811 = 8.11\%$

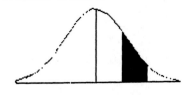

15   17.5 18.5

b. $\mu = 0.8(50) = 40$
$\sigma = \sqrt{(50)(0.8)(0.2)} = 2.83$

$z = \frac{43.5 - 40}{2.83} = 1.24$ area = 0.3925

$z = \frac{44.5 - 40}{2.83} = 1.59$ area = 0.4441

$P(43.5 < X < 44.5) = 0.4441 - 0.3925$
$= 0.0516$ or 5.16%

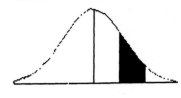

40   43.5 44.5

c. $\mu = 0.1(100) = 10$
$\sigma = \sqrt{(0.1)(0.9)(100)} = 3$

$z = \frac{11.5 - 10}{3} = 0.50$ area = 0.1915

$z = \frac{12.5 - 10}{3} = 0.83$ area = 0.2967

$P(11.5 < X < 12.5) = 0.2967 - 0.1915$
$= 0.1052$ or 10.52%

7-124. continued

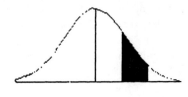

10   11.5 12.5

d. $\mu = 10(0.5) = 5$
$\sigma = \sqrt{(0.5)(0.5)(10)} = 1.58$

$z = \frac{6.5 - 5}{1.58} = 0.95$ area = 0.3289

$P(X \geq 6.5) = 0.5 - 0.3289 = 0.1711$ or
17.11%

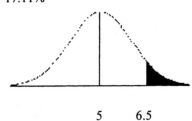

5   6.5

e. $\mu = 20(0.7) = 14$
$\sigma = \sqrt{(20)(0.7)(0.3)} = 2.05$

$z = \frac{12.5 - 14}{2.05} = -0.73$ area = 0.2673

$P(X \leq 12.5) = 0.5 - 0.2673 = 0.2327$ or
23.37%

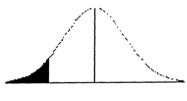

12.5   14

f. $\mu = 50(0.6) = 30$
$\sigma = \sqrt{(50)(0.6)(0.4)} = 3.46$

$z = \frac{40.5 - 30}{3.46} = 3.03$ area = 0.4988

$P(X \leq 40.5) = 0.5 + 0.4988 = 0.9988$ or
99.88%

7-124. continued

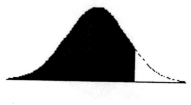

30   40.5

7-129. continued

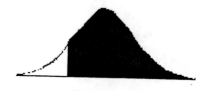

5.5   12

7-125.

a. $np = 20(0.50) = 10 \geq 5$ Yes
$\ \ nq = 20(0.50) = 10 \geq 5$

b. $np = 10(0.60) = 6 \geq 5$ No
$\ \ nq = 10(0.40) = 4 < 5$

c. $np = 40(0.90) = 36 \geq 5$ No
$\ \ nq = 40(0.10) = 4 < 5$

d. $np = 50(0.20) = 10 \geq 5$ Yes
$\ \ nq = 50(0.80) = 40 \geq 5$

e. $np = 30(0.80) = 24 \geq 5$ Yes
$\ \ nq = 30(0.20) = 6 \geq 5$

f. $np = 20(0.85) = 17 \geq 5$ No
$\ \ nq = 20(0.15) = 3 \ > 5$

7-127.

$p = \frac{2}{5} = 0.4 \qquad \mu = 400(0.4) = 160$

$\sigma = \sqrt{(400)(0.4)(0.6)} = 9.8$

$z = \frac{169.5 - 160}{9.8} = 0.97 \qquad$ area $= 0.3340$

$P(X > 169.5) = 0.5 - 0.3340 = 0.1660$ or 16.6%

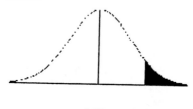

160   169.5

7-129.

$\mu = 80(0.15) = 12$

$\sigma = \sqrt{(80)(0.15)(0.85)} = 3.19$

a. $z = \frac{5.5 - 12}{3.19} = -2.04 \qquad$ area $= 0.4793$

$P(X > 5.5) = 0.5 + 0.4793 = 0.9793$ or 97.93%

b. $z = \frac{4.5 - 12}{3.19} = -2.35 \qquad$ area $= 0.4906$

$P(X < 4.5) = 0.5 - 0.4906 = 0.0094$ or 0.94%

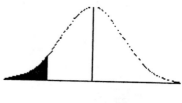

4.5   12

7-131.

$\mu = 100(0.18) = 18$

$\sigma = \sqrt{(100)(0.18)(0.82)} = 3.84$

$z = \frac{17.5 - 18}{3.84} = -0.13 \qquad$ area $= 0.0517$

$z = \frac{18.5 - 18}{3.84} = 0.13 \qquad$ area $= 0.0517$

$P(17.5 < X < 18.5) = 0.0517 + 0.0517$
$= 0.1034$ or 10.34%

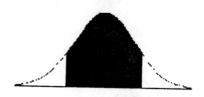

17.5   18   18.5

7-133.

$\mu = 180(0.03) = 5.4$

$\sigma = \sqrt{(180)(0.03)(0.97)} = 2.29$

$z = \frac{6.5 - 5.4}{2.29} = 0.48 \qquad$ area $= 0.1844$

$P(X < 6.5) = 0.5 + 0.1844 = 0.6844$ or 68.44%

7-133. continued

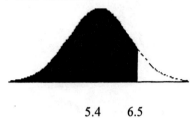

5.4   6.5

7-135.

$\mu = 400(0.3) = 120$

$\sigma = \sqrt{(400)(0.3)(0.7)} = 9.17$

$z = \frac{99.5 - 120}{9.17} = -2.24$

$P(X > 99.5) = 0.5 + 0.4875 = 0.9875$ or 98.75%

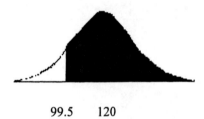

99.5   120

7-137.

a. 0.4744

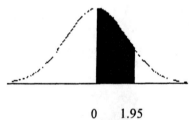

0   1.95

b. 0.1443

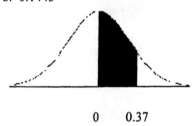

0   0.37

c. $0.4664 - 0.4066 = 0.0598$

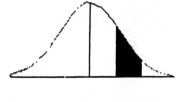

0   1.32 1.82

7-137. continued

d. $0.3531 + 0.4798 = 0.8329$

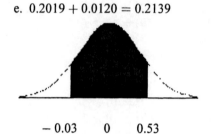

-1.05   0   2.05

e. $0.2019 + 0.0120 = 0.2139$

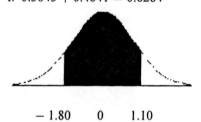

-0.03   0   0.53

f. $0.3643 + 0.4641 = 0.8284$

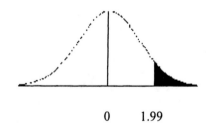

-1.80   0   1.10

g. $0.5 - 0.4767 = 0.0233$

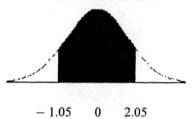

0   1.99

h. $0.5 + 0.4131 = 0.9131$

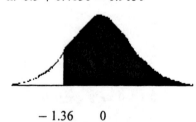

-1.36   0

56

7-137. continued
i. $0.5 - 0.4817 = 0.0183$

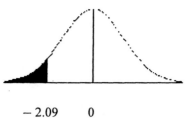

$-2.09 \quad 0$

j. $0.5 + 0.4535 = 0.9535$

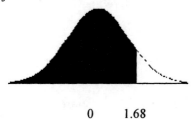

$0 \quad 1.68$

7-139.
a. $z_1 = \frac{X-\mu}{\sigma} = \frac{1-1.5}{0.3} = -1.67$
area $= 0.4525$

$z_2 = \frac{1.3-1.5}{0.3} = -0.67 \quad$ area $= 0.2486$

$P(-1.67 < z < -0.67) = 0.4525 - 0.2486 = 0.2039$ or 20.39%

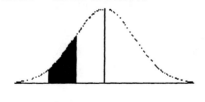

$1.0 \quad 1.3 \quad 1.5$

b. $z = \frac{2.2-1.5}{0.3} = 2.33 \quad$ area $= 0.4901$

$P(z > 2.33) = 0.5 - 0.4901 = 0.0099$ or 0.99%

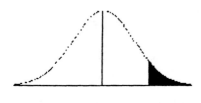

$1.5 \quad 2.2$

c. $z = \frac{1.1-1.5}{0.3} = -1.33 \quad$ area $= 0.4082$

$P(z < -1.33) = 0.5 - 0.4082 = 0.0918$ or 9.18%

7-139. continued

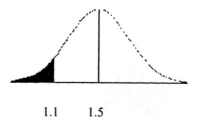

$1.1 \quad 1.5$

7-141.
a. $z_1 = \frac{5-5.6}{0.8} = -0.75 \quad$ area $= 0.2734$

$z_2 = \frac{6-5.6}{0.8} = 0.5 \quad$ area $= 0.1915$

$P(-0.75 < z < 0.5) = 0.2734 + 0.1915 = 0.4649$ or 46.49%

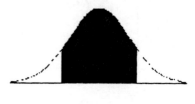

$5 \quad 5.6 \quad 6$

b. $z = \frac{4-5.6}{0.8} = -2.00 \quad$ area $= 0.4772$

$P(z < -2.00) = 0.5 - 0.4772 = 0.0228$ or 2.28%

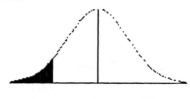

$4 \quad 5.6$

c. $z = \frac{6.3-5.6}{0.8} = 0.88 \quad$ area $= 0.3106$

$P(z > 0.88) = 0.5 - 0.3106 = 0.1894$ or 18.94%

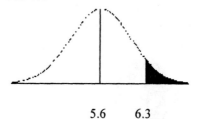

$5.6 \quad 6.3$

7-143.
a. $z_1 = \frac{600-617}{52} = -0.33 \quad$ area $= 0.1293$

$z_2 = \frac{700-617}{52} = 1.60 \quad$ area $= 0.4452$

7-143. continued

$P(-0.33 < z < 1.60) = 0.1293 + 0.4452$
$= 0.5745$ or 57.45%

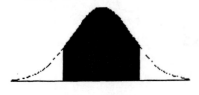

600   617   700

b. $z = \frac{575-617}{52} = -0.81$ area $= 0.2910$

$P(z < -0.81) = 0.5 - 0.2910 = 0.2090$ or
20.9%

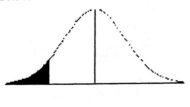

575   617

c. $z = \frac{624-617}{52} = 0.13$ area $= 0.0517$

$P(z > 0.13) = 0.5 - 0.0517 = 0.4483$ or
44.83%

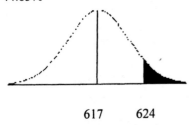

617   624

7-145.

The middle 40% means that 20% of the area
is on either side of the mean. The
corresponding z scores are ± 0.52.
$X_1 = 100 + (0.52)(15) = 107.8$
$X_2 = 100 + (-0.52)(15) = 92.2$
The scores should be between 92.2 and
107.8.

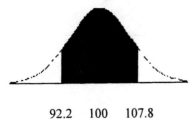

92.2   100   107.8

7-147.

$z = \frac{11-12.2}{\frac{2.3}{\sqrt{12}}} = -1.81$ area $= 0.4649$

$P(\overline{X} < 11) = 0.5 - 0.4649 = 0.0351$ or
3.51%

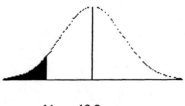

11   12.2

7-149.

$\mu = 200(0.18) = 36$
$\sigma = \sqrt{(200)(0.18)(0.82)} = 5.43$

$z = \frac{40.5-36}{5.43} = 0.83$ area $= 0.2967$

$P(X > 40.5) = 0.5 - 0.2967 = 0.2033$ or
20.33%

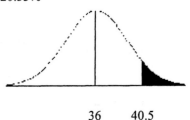

36   40.5

7-151.

$\mu = 200(0.2) = 40$
$\sigma = \sqrt{(200)(0.2)(0.8)} = 5.66$

$z = \frac{49.5-40}{5.66} = 1.68$ area $= 0.4535$

$P(X \geq 49.5) = 0.5 - 0.4535 = 0.0465$ or
4.65%

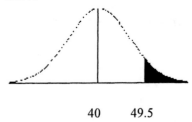

40   49.5

Quiz
1. False, the total area is equal to one.
2. True
3. True
4. True
5. False, the area is positive.
6. False, it applies to means taken from the
same population.

7. a
8. a
9. b
10. b
11. c
12. 0.5
13. sampling error
14. the population mean
15. the standard error of the mean
16. 5
17. 5%
18. the areas are:

a. 0.4332   f. 0.8079
b. 0.3944   g. 0.5401
c. 0.0344   h. 0.6003
d. 0.1029   i. 0.017
e. 0.2912   j. 0.991

19. the probabilities are:

a. 0.4846   f. 0.0384
b. 0.4693   g. 0.0089
c. 0.9334   h. 0.9582
d. 0.0188   i. 0.9788
e. 0.7461   j. 0.8461

20. the probabilities are:

a. 0.0531   c. 0.1056
b. 0.1056   d. 0.0994

21. the probabilities are:

a. 0.0668   c. 0.1056
b. 0.1056   d. 0.0994

22. the probabilities are:

a. 0.4525   c. 0.3707
b. 0.3707   d. 0.019

23. the probabilities are:

a. 0.0013   c. 0.0081
b. 0.5   d. 0.5511

24. the probabilities are:

a. 0.0037   c. 0.0038
b. 0.0228   d. 0.3232

25. 8.804 cm
26. The lowest acceptable score is 121.24.
27. 0.015
28. 0.9738
29. 0.1977
30. 0.0681
31. 0.0294
32. 0.0606

Note: Answers may vary slightly due to rounding.

8-1.
A point estimate of a parameter specifies a specific value such as $\mu = 87$, whereas an interval estimate specifies a range of values for the parameter such as $84 < \mu < 90$. The advantage of an interval estimate is that a specific confidence level (say 95%) can be selected, and one can be 95% confident that the parameter being estimated lies in the interval.

8-3.
The maximum error of estimate is the likely range of values to the right or left of the statistic in which may contain the parameter.

8-5.
A good estimator should be unbiased, consistent, and relatively efficient.

8-7.
To determine sample size, the maximum error of estimate and the degree of confidence must be specified and the population standard deviation must be known.

8-9.
a. 2.58   d. 1.65
b. 2.33   e. 1.88
c. 1.96

8-11.
a. $\overline{X} - z_{\frac{\alpha}{2}}\left(\frac{s}{\sqrt{n}}\right) < \mu < \overline{X} + z_{\frac{\alpha}{2}}\left(\frac{s}{\sqrt{n}}\right)$
$82 - (1.96)\left(\frac{15}{\sqrt{35}}\right) < \mu < 82 + (1.96)\left(\frac{15}{\sqrt{35}}\right)$
$82 - 4.97 < \mu < 82 + 4.97$
$77 < \mu < 87$

b. $82 - (2.58)\left(\frac{15}{\sqrt{35}}\right) < \mu < 82 + (2.58)\left(\frac{15}{\sqrt{35}}\right)$
$82 - 6.54 < \mu < 82 + 6.54$
$75 < \mu < 89$

c. The 99% confidence interval is larger because the confidence level is larger.

8-13.
a. $\overline{X} - z_{\frac{\alpha}{2}}\left(\frac{\sigma}{\sqrt{n}}\right) < \mu < \overline{X} + z_{\frac{\alpha}{2}}\left(\frac{\sigma}{\sqrt{n}}\right)$
$12.6 - 1.65\left(\frac{2.5}{\sqrt{40}}\right) < \mu < 12.6 + 1.65\left(\frac{2.5}{\sqrt{40}}\right)$
$12.6 - 0.652 < \mu < 12.6 + 0.652$
$11.9 < \mu < 13.3$

8-13. continued
b. It would be highly unlikely since this is far above 13.3 minutes.

8-15.
a. $\overline{X} - z_{\frac{\alpha}{2}}\left(\frac{s}{\sqrt{n}}\right) < \mu < \overline{X} + z_{\frac{\alpha}{2}}\left(\frac{s}{\sqrt{n}}\right)$
$\$18.50 - 1.65\left(\frac{1.56}{\sqrt{49}}\right) < \mu <$
$\qquad \$18.50 + 1.65\left(\frac{1.56}{\sqrt{49}}\right)$

$\$18.50 - 0.37 < \mu < \$18.50 + 0.37$
$\$18.13 < \mu < \$18.87$

8-17.
$\overline{X} = 3222.43 \qquad s = 3480.11$
$3222.43 - 1.645\left(\frac{3480.11}{\sqrt{40}}\right) < \mu < 3222.43 +$
$\qquad 1.645\left(\frac{3480.11}{\sqrt{40}}\right)$
$2317.3 < \mu < 4127.5$

8-19.
$\overline{X} - z_{\frac{\alpha}{2}}\left(\frac{s}{\sqrt{n}}\right) < \mu < \overline{X} + z_{\frac{\alpha}{2}}\left(\frac{s}{\sqrt{n}}\right)$
$61.2 - 1.96\left(\frac{7.9}{\sqrt{84}}\right) < \mu < 61.2 + 1.96\left(\frac{7.9}{\sqrt{84}}\right)$
$61.2 - 1.69 < \mu < 61.2 + 1.69$
$59.5 < \mu < 62.9$

8-21.
$n = \left[\frac{z_{\frac{\alpha}{2}} \cdot \sigma}{E}\right]^2 = \left[\frac{(2.58)(2.6)}{1}\right]^2$
$= (6.708)^2 = 44.9973$ or 45

8-23.
$n = \left[\frac{z_{\frac{\alpha}{2}} \cdot \sigma}{E}\right]^2 = \left[\frac{(1.96)(2.5)}{1}\right]^2$
$= (4.9)^2 = 24.01$ or 25

8-25.
$n = \left[\frac{z_{\frac{\alpha}{2}} \cdot \sigma}{E}\right]^2 = \left[\frac{(1.65)(8)}{6}\right]^2$
$= (2.2)^2 = 4.84$ or 5

8-27.
W. S. Gossett

8-29.
The t-distribution should be used when σ is unknown and $n < 30$.

8-30.
a. 2.898 where d. f. $= 17$
b. 2.074 where d. f. $= 22$
c. 2.624 where d. f. $= 14$
d. 1.833 where d. f. $= 9$

8-30. continued

e. 2.093 where d. f. $= 19$

8-31.

$\overline{X} - t_{\frac{\alpha}{2}}(\frac{s}{\sqrt{n}}) < \mu < \overline{X} + t_{\frac{\alpha}{2}}(\frac{s}{\sqrt{n}})$

$16 - (2.861)(\frac{2}{\sqrt{20}}) < \mu < 16 + (2.861)(\frac{2}{\sqrt{20}})$

$16 - 1.28 < \mu < 16 + 1.28$

$15 < \mu < 17$

8-33.

$\overline{X} = 33.4 \quad s = 28.7$

$\overline{X} - t_{\frac{\alpha}{2}}(\frac{s}{\sqrt{n}}) < \mu < \overline{X} + t_{\frac{\alpha}{2}}(\frac{s}{\sqrt{n}})$

$33.4 - 1.746(\frac{28.7}{\sqrt{17}}) < \mu < 33.4 + 1.746(\frac{28.7}{\sqrt{17}})$

$33.4 - 12.2 < \mu < 33.4 + 12.2$

$21.2 < \mu < 45.6$

The point estimate is 33.4 and is close to the actual population mean of 32, which is within the 90% confidence interval. The mean may not be the best estimate since the data value 132 is large and possibly an outlier.

8-35.

$\overline{X} - t_{\frac{\alpha}{2}}(\frac{s}{\sqrt{n}}) < \mu < \overline{X} + t_{\frac{\alpha}{2}}(\frac{s}{\sqrt{n}})$

$12{,}200 - 2.571(\frac{200}{\sqrt{6}}) < \mu <$

$\quad 12{,}200 + 2.571(\frac{200}{\sqrt{6}})$

$12{,}200 - 209.921 < \mu < 12{,}200 + 209.921$

$11{,}990 < \mu < 12{,}410$

8-37.

$\overline{X} - t_{\frac{\alpha}{2}}(\frac{s}{\sqrt{n}}) < \mu < \overline{X} + t_{\frac{\alpha}{2}}(\frac{s}{\sqrt{n}})$

$9.3 - 1.703(\frac{2}{\sqrt{28}}) < \mu < 9.3 + 1.703(\frac{2}{\sqrt{28}})$

$9.3 - 0.644 < \mu < 9.3 + 0.644$

$8.7 < \mu < 9.9$

8-39.

$\overline{X} - t_{\frac{\alpha}{2}}(\frac{s}{\sqrt{n}}) < \mu < \overline{X} + t_{\frac{\alpha}{2}}(\frac{s}{\sqrt{n}})$

$18.53 - 2.064(\frac{3}{\sqrt{25}}) < \mu <$

$\quad 18.53 + 2.064(\frac{3}{\sqrt{25}})$

$18.53 - 1.238 < \mu < 18.53 + 1.238$

$17.29 < \mu < 19.77$

8-41.

$\overline{X} - t_{\frac{\alpha}{2}}(\frac{s}{\sqrt{n}}) < \mu < \overline{X} + t_{\frac{\alpha}{2}}(\frac{s}{\sqrt{n}})$

$115 - 2.571(\frac{6}{\sqrt{6}}) < \mu < 115 + 2.571(\frac{6}{\sqrt{6}})$

$115 - 6.298 < \mu < 115 + 6.298$

$109 < \mu < 121$

8-43.

$\overline{X} - t_{\frac{\alpha}{2}}(\frac{s}{\sqrt{n}}) < \mu < \overline{X} + t_{\frac{\alpha}{2}}(\frac{s}{\sqrt{n}})$

$86.9 - 2.650(\frac{111.5}{\sqrt{14}}) < \mu <$

$\quad 86.9 + 2.650(\frac{111.5}{\sqrt{14}})$

$86.9 - 79.0 < \mu < 86.9 + 79.0$

$7.9 < \mu < 165.9$

The 98% confidence interval includes the population mean of $65.70.

8-45.

$\overline{X} - t_{\frac{\alpha}{2}}(\frac{s}{\sqrt{n}}) < \mu < \overline{X} + t_{\frac{\alpha}{2}}(\frac{s}{\sqrt{n}})$

$\$58{,}219 - 2.052(\frac{56}{\sqrt{28}}) < \mu <$

$\quad \$58{,}219 + 2.052(\frac{56}{\sqrt{28}})$

$\$58{,}197 < \mu < \$58{,}241$

8-47.

a. $\hat{p} = \frac{40}{80} = 0.5 \qquad \hat{q} = \frac{40}{80} = 0.5$

b. $\hat{p} = \frac{90}{200} = 0.45 \qquad \hat{q} = \frac{110}{200} = 0.55$

c. $\hat{p} = \frac{60}{130} = 0.46 \qquad \hat{q} = \frac{70}{130} = 0.54$

d. $\hat{p} = \frac{35}{60} = 0.58 \hat{q} = \frac{25}{60} = 0.42$

e. $\hat{p} = \frac{43}{95} = 0.45 \qquad \hat{q} = \frac{52}{95} = 0.55$

8-48.

For each part, change the percent to a decimal by dividing by 100, and find $\hat{q}$ using $\hat{q} = 1 - \hat{p}$.

a. $\hat{p} = 0.12 \qquad \hat{q} = 1 - 0.12 = 0.88$

b. $\hat{p} = 0.29 \qquad \hat{q} = 1 - 0.29 = 0.71$

c. $\hat{p} = 0.65 \qquad \hat{q} = 1 - 0.65 = 0.35$

d. $\hat{p} = 0.53 \qquad \hat{q} = 1 - 0.53 = 0.47$

e. $\hat{p} = 0.67 \qquad \hat{q} = 1 - 0.67 = 0.33$

8-49.

$\hat{p} = 0.39 \qquad\qquad \hat{q} = 0.61$

$\hat{p} - (z_{\frac{\alpha}{2}})\sqrt{\frac{\hat{p}\hat{q}}{n}} < p < \hat{p} + (z_{\frac{\alpha}{2}})\sqrt{\frac{\hat{p}\hat{q}}{n}}$

$0.39 - (1.96)\sqrt{\frac{(0.39)(0.61)}{1500}} < p <$

$\quad 0.39 + (1.96)\sqrt{\frac{(0.39)(0.61)}{1500}}$

$0.39 - 0.025 < p < 0.39 + 0.025$

$0.365 < p < 0.415$

8-51.

$\hat{p} = 0.65 \qquad\qquad \hat{q} = 0.35$

$\hat{p} - (z_{\frac{\alpha}{2}})\sqrt{\frac{\hat{p}\hat{q}}{n}} < p < \hat{p} + (z_{\frac{\alpha}{2}})\sqrt{\frac{\hat{p}\hat{q}}{n}}$

8-51. continued

$$0.65 - 1.96\sqrt{\frac{(0.65)(0.35)}{100}} < p <$$

$$0.65 + 1.96\sqrt{\frac{(0.65)(0.35)}{100}}$$

$$0.65 - 0.093 < p < 0.65 + 0.093$$
$$0.557 < p < 0.743$$

8-53.
$$\hat{p} = 0.84 \qquad \hat{q} = 0.16$$
$$\hat{p} - (z_{\frac{\alpha}{2}})\sqrt{\frac{\hat{p}\hat{q}}{n}} < p < \hat{p} + (z_{\frac{\alpha}{2}})\sqrt{\frac{\hat{p}\hat{q}}{n}}$$
$$0.84 - 1.65\sqrt{\frac{(0.84)(0.16)}{200}} < p <$$
$$0.84 + 1.65\sqrt{\frac{(0.84)(0.16)}{200}}$$
$$0.84 - 0.043 < p < 0.84 + 0.043$$
$$0.797 < p < 0.883$$

8-55.
$$\hat{p} = 0.23 \qquad \hat{q} = 0.77$$
$$\hat{p} - (z_{\frac{\alpha}{2}})\sqrt{\frac{\hat{p}\hat{q}}{n}} < p < \hat{p} + (z_{\frac{\alpha}{2}})\sqrt{\frac{\hat{p}\hat{q}}{n}}$$
$$0.23 - 2.58\sqrt{\frac{(0.23)(0.77)}{200}} < p <$$
$$0.23 + 2.58\sqrt{\frac{(0.23)(0.77)}{200}}$$
$$0.23 - 0.077 < p < 0.23 + 0.077$$
$$0.153 < p < 0.307$$
The statement that one in five or 20% of 13 to 14 year olds is a sometime smoker is within the interval.

8-57.
$$\hat{p} = \frac{40}{90} = 0.44 \qquad \hat{q} = \frac{50}{90} = 0.56$$
$$\hat{p} - (z_{\frac{\alpha}{2}})\sqrt{\frac{\hat{p}\hat{q}}{n}} < p < \hat{p} + (z_{\frac{\alpha}{2}})\sqrt{\frac{\hat{p}\hat{q}}{n}}$$
$$0.44 - 1.96\sqrt{\frac{(0.44)(0.56)}{90}} < p <$$
$$0.44 + 1.96\sqrt{\frac{(0.44)(0.56)}{90}}$$
$$0.44 - 0.103 < p < 0.44 + 0.103$$
$$0.337 < p < 0.543$$

8-59.
$$\hat{p} = 0.25 \qquad \hat{q} = 0.75$$
$$\hat{p} - (z_{\frac{\alpha}{2}})\sqrt{\frac{\hat{p}\hat{q}}{n}} < p < \hat{p} + (z_{\frac{\alpha}{2}})\sqrt{\frac{\hat{p}\hat{q}}{n}}$$
$$0.25 - 2.33\sqrt{\frac{(0.25)(0.75)}{100}} < p <$$
$$0.25 + 2.33\sqrt{\frac{(0.25)(0.75)}{100}}$$
$$0.25 - 0.101 < p < 0.25 + 0.101$$
$$0.149 < p < 0.351$$

8-61.
a. $\hat{p} = 0.25 \qquad \hat{q} = 0.75$

$$n = \hat{p}\,\hat{q}\left[\frac{z_{\frac{\alpha}{2}}}{E}\right]^2 = (0.25)(0.75)\left[\frac{2.58}{0.02}\right]^2$$

8-61. continued
$$= 3120.1875 \text{ or } 3121$$

b. $\hat{p} = 0.5 \qquad \hat{q} = 0.5$

$$n = \hat{p}\,\hat{q}\left[\frac{z_{\frac{\alpha}{2}}}{E}\right]^2 = (0.5)(0.5)\left[\frac{2.58}{0.02}\right]^2$$

$$n = 4160.25 \text{ or } 4161$$

8-63.
a. $\hat{p} = \frac{30}{300} = 0.1 \qquad \hat{q} = \frac{270}{300} = 0.9$

$$n = \hat{p}\,\hat{q}\left[\frac{z_{\frac{\alpha}{2}}}{E}\right]^2 = (0.1)(0.9)\left[\frac{1.65}{0.05}\right]^2$$

$$= 98.01 \text{ or } 99$$

b. $\hat{p} = 0.5 \qquad \hat{q} = 0.5$

$$n = \hat{p}\,\hat{q}\left[\frac{z_{\frac{\alpha}{2}}}{E}\right]^2 = (0.5)(0.5)\left[\frac{1.65}{0.05}\right]^2$$

$$n = 272.25 \text{ or } 273$$

8-65.
$$\hat{p} = 0.5 \qquad \hat{q} = 0.5$$
$$n = \hat{p}\,\hat{q}\left[\frac{z_{\frac{\alpha}{2}}}{E}\right]^2$$
$$600 = (0.5)(0.5)\left[\frac{z}{0.04}\right]^2$$
$$1.96 = z$$
The degree of confidence is 95%.

8-67.
$$\chi^2$$

8-69.

	χ^2_{left}	χ^2_{right}
a.	6.262	27.488
b.	0.711	9.488
c.	8.643	42.796
d.	15.308	44.461
e.	5.892	22.362

8-71.
$$\frac{(n-1)s^2}{\chi^2_{right}} < \sigma^2 < \frac{(n-1)s^2}{\chi^2_{left}}$$

$$\frac{26(6.8)^2}{38.885} < \sigma^2 < \frac{26(6.8)^2}{15.379}$$

$$30.9 < \sigma^2 < 78.2$$
$$5.6 < \sigma < 8.8$$

8-73.

$s^2 = 0.80997$ or 0.81

$$\frac{(n-1)s^2}{\chi^2_{right}} < \sigma^2 < \frac{(n-1)s^2}{\chi^2_{left}}$$

$$\frac{19(0.81)}{38.582} < \sigma^2 < \frac{19(0.81)}{6.844}$$

$0.40 < \sigma^2 < 2.25$

$0.6 < \sigma < 1.5$

8-75.

$$\frac{(n-1)s^2}{\chi^2_{right}} < \sigma^2 < \frac{(n-1)s^2}{\chi^2_{left}}$$

$$\frac{14(1.6)^2}{29.141} < \sigma^2 < \frac{14(1.6)^2}{4.660}$$

$1.2 < \sigma^2 < 7.7$

$1.1 < \sigma < 2.8$

8-77.

$$\frac{(n-1)s^2}{\chi^2_{right}} < \sigma^2 < \frac{(n-1)s^2}{\chi^2_{left}}$$

$$\frac{27(5.2)^2}{43.194} < \sigma^2 < \frac{27(5.2)^2}{14.573}$$

$16.9 < \sigma^2 < 50.1$

$4.1 < \sigma < 7.1$

8-79.

$$s - z_{\frac{\alpha}{2}}\left(\frac{s}{\sqrt{2n}}\right) < \sigma < s + z_{\frac{\alpha}{2}}\left(\frac{s}{\sqrt{2n}}\right)$$

$$18 - 1.96\left(\frac{18}{\sqrt{400}}\right) < \sigma < 18 + 1.96\left(\frac{18}{\sqrt{400}}\right)$$

$16.2 < \sigma < 19.8$

8-81.

$$\overline{X} - z_{\frac{\alpha}{2}}\left(\frac{s}{\sqrt{n}}\right) < \mu < \overline{X} + z_{\frac{\alpha}{2}}\left(\frac{s}{\sqrt{n}}\right)$$

$$2.6 - 1.96\left(\frac{0.4}{\sqrt{36}}\right) < \mu < 2.6 + 1.96\left(\frac{0.4}{\sqrt{36}}\right)$$

$2.5 < \mu < 2.7$

8-83.

$$\overline{X} - z_{\frac{\alpha}{2}}\left(\frac{s}{\sqrt{n}}\right) < \mu < \overline{X} + z_{\frac{\alpha}{2}}\left(\frac{s}{\sqrt{n}}\right)$$

$$7.5 - 1.96\left(\frac{0.8}{\sqrt{1500}}\right) < \mu < 7.5 + 1.96\left(\frac{0.8}{\sqrt{1500}}\right)$$

$7.46 < \mu < 7.54$

8-85.

$$\overline{X} - t_{\frac{\alpha}{2}}\left(\frac{s}{\sqrt{n}}\right) < \mu < \overline{X} + t_{\frac{\alpha}{2}}\left(\frac{s}{\sqrt{n}}\right)$$

8-85. continued

$$28 - 2.132\left(\frac{3}{\sqrt{5}}\right) < \mu < 28 + 2.132\left(\frac{3}{\sqrt{5}}\right)$$

$25 < \mu < 31$

8-87.

$$n = \left[\frac{z_{\frac{\alpha}{2}} \cdot \sigma}{E}\right]^2 = \left[\frac{1.65(80)}{25}\right]^2$$

$$= (5.28)^2 = 27.88 \text{ or } 28$$

8-89.

$\hat{p} = 0.4 \qquad \hat{q} = 0.6$

$$\hat{p} - (z_{\frac{\alpha}{2}})\sqrt{\frac{\hat{p}\hat{q}}{n}} < p < \hat{p} + (z_{\frac{\alpha}{2}})\sqrt{\frac{\hat{p}\hat{q}}{n}}$$

$$0.4 - 1.65\sqrt{\frac{(0.4)(0.6)}{200}} < p <$$
$$0.4 + 1.65\sqrt{\frac{(0.4)(0.6)}{200}}$$

$0.4 - 0.057 < p < 0.4 + 0.057$

$0.343 < p < 0.457$

8-91.

$\hat{p} = 0.18 \qquad \hat{q} = 0.82$

$$n = \hat{p}\,\hat{q}\left[\frac{z_{\frac{\alpha}{2}}}{E}\right]^2 = (0.18)(0.82)\left[\frac{1.96}{0.02}\right]^2$$

$$= 0.1476(98)^2 = 1417.55 \text{ or } 1418$$

8-93.

$$\frac{(n-1)s^2}{\chi^2_{right}} < \sigma^2 < \frac{(n-1)s^2}{\chi^2_{left}}$$

$$\frac{(28-1)(0.34)^2}{49.645} < \sigma^2 < \frac{(28-1)(0.34)^2}{11.808}$$

$0.06287 < \sigma^2 < 0.26433$

$0.25 < \sigma < 0.51$

8-95.

$$\frac{(n-1)s^2}{\chi^2_{right}} < \sigma^2 < \frac{(n-1)s^2}{\chi^2_{left}}$$

$$\frac{(15-1)(8.6)}{23.685} < \sigma^2 < \frac{(15-1)(8.6)}{6.571}$$

$5.1 < \sigma^2 < 18.3$

Quiz
1. True
2. True

3. False, it is consistent if, as sample size increases, the estimator approaches the parameter being estimated.
4. True
5. b
6. a
7. b
8. unbiased, consistent, relatively efficient
9. maximum error of estimate
10. point
11. 90, 95, 99

12. $\overline{X} - z_{\frac{\alpha}{2}}(\frac{s}{\sqrt{n}}) < \mu < \overline{X} + z_{\frac{\alpha}{2}}(\frac{s}{\sqrt{n}})$

$\$23.45 - 1.65(\frac{2.80}{\sqrt{49}}) < \mu <$
$\quad \$23.45 + 1.65(\frac{2.80}{\sqrt{49}})$

$\$22.79 < \mu < \$24.11$

13. $\overline{X} - t_{\frac{\alpha}{2}}(\frac{s}{\sqrt{n}}) < \mu < \overline{X} + t_{\frac{\alpha}{2}}(\frac{s}{\sqrt{n}})$

$\$44.80 - 2.093(\frac{3.53}{\sqrt{20}}) < \mu <$
$\quad \$44.80 + 2.093(\frac{3.53}{\sqrt{20}})$

$\$43.15 < \mu < \$46.45$

14. $\overline{X} - z_{\frac{\alpha}{2}}(\frac{s}{\sqrt{n}}) < \mu < \overline{X} + z_{\frac{\alpha}{2}}(\frac{s}{\sqrt{n}})$

$\$4150 - 2.58(\frac{480}{\sqrt{40}}) < \mu <$
$\quad \$4150 + 2.58(\frac{480}{\sqrt{40}})$

$3954 < \mu < 4346$

15. $\overline{X} - t_{\frac{\alpha}{2}}(\frac{s}{\sqrt{n}}) < \mu < \overline{X} + t_{\frac{\alpha}{2}}(\frac{s}{\sqrt{n}})$

$48.6 - 2.262(\frac{4.1}{\sqrt{10}}) < \mu < 48.6 + 2.262(\frac{4.1}{\sqrt{10}})$

$45.7 < \mu < 51.5$

16. $\overline{X} - t_{\frac{\alpha}{2}}(\frac{s}{\sqrt{n}}) < \mu < \overline{X} + t_{\frac{\alpha}{2}}(\frac{s}{\sqrt{n}})$

$438 - 3.499(\frac{16}{\sqrt{8}}) < \mu < 438 + 3.499(\frac{16}{\sqrt{8}})$

$418 < \mu < 458$

17. $\overline{X} - t_{\frac{\alpha}{2}}(\frac{s}{\sqrt{n}}) < \mu < \overline{X} + t_{\frac{\alpha}{2}}(\frac{s}{\sqrt{n}})$

$31 - 2.353(\frac{4}{\sqrt{4}}) < \mu < 31 + 2.353(\frac{4}{\sqrt{4}})$

17. continued
$26 < \mu < 36$

18. $n = \left[\frac{z_{\frac{\alpha}{2}}\sigma}{E}\right]^2 = \left[\frac{2.58(2.6)}{0.5}\right]^2$

$\quad = 179.98$ or 180

19. $n = \left[\frac{z_{\frac{\alpha}{2}}\sigma}{E}\right]^2 = \left[\frac{1.65(900)}{300}\right]^2$

$\quad = 24.5$ or 25

20. $\hat{p} - (z_{\frac{\alpha}{2}})\sqrt{\frac{\hat{p}\hat{q}}{n}} < p < \hat{p} + (z_{\frac{\alpha}{2}})\sqrt{\frac{\hat{p}\hat{q}}{n}}$

$\hat{p} = \frac{53}{75} = 0.707 \quad \hat{q} = \frac{22}{75} = 0.293$

$0.71 - 1.96\sqrt{\frac{(0.707)(0.293)}{75}} < p <$
$\quad 0.71 + 1.96\sqrt{\frac{(0.707)(0.293)}{75}}$

$0.604 < p < 0.810$

21. $\hat{p} - (z_{\frac{\alpha}{2}})\sqrt{\frac{\hat{p}\hat{q}}{n}} < p < \hat{p} + (z_{\frac{\alpha}{2}})\sqrt{\frac{\hat{p}\hat{q}}{n}}$

$0.36 - 1.65\sqrt{\frac{(0.36)(0.64)}{150}} < p <$
$\quad 0.36 + 1.65\sqrt{\frac{(0.36)(0.64)}{150}}$

$0.295 < p < 0.425$

22. $\hat{p} - (z_{\frac{\alpha}{2}})\sqrt{\frac{\hat{p}\hat{q}}{n}} < p < \hat{p} + (z_{\frac{\alpha}{2}})\sqrt{\frac{\hat{p}\hat{q}}{n}}$

$0.444 - 1.96\sqrt{\frac{(0.444)(0.556)}{90}} < p <$
$\quad 0.444 + 1.96\sqrt{\frac{(0.444)(0.556)}{90}}$

$0.341 < p < 0.557$

23. $n = \hat{p}\hat{q}\left[\frac{z_{\frac{\alpha}{2}}}{E}\right]^2$

$\quad = (0.15)(0.85)\left[\frac{1.96}{0.03}\right]^2$

$\quad = 544.22$ or 545

24. $\frac{(n-1)s^2}{\chi^2_{right}} < \sigma^2 < \frac{(n-1)s^2}{\chi^2_{left}}$

$\frac{24(9)^2}{39.364} < \sigma^2 < \frac{24(9)^2}{12.401}$

$49.4 < \sigma^2 < 156.8$

24. continued

$7 < \sigma < 13$

25. $\dfrac{(n-1)s^2}{\chi^2_{right}} < \sigma^2 < \dfrac{(n-1)s^2}{\chi^2_{left}}$

$\dfrac{26(6.8)^2}{38.885} < \sigma^2 < \dfrac{26(6.8)^2}{15.379}$

$30.9 < \sigma^2 < 78.2$

$5.6 < \sigma < 8.8$

26. $\dfrac{(n-1)s^2}{\chi^2_{right}} < \sigma^2 < \dfrac{(n-1)s^2}{\chi^2_{left}}$

$\dfrac{19(2.3)^2}{30.144} < \sigma^2 < \dfrac{19(2.3)^2}{10.177}$

$3.33 < \sigma^2 < 10$

$1.8 < \sigma < 3.2$

Note: Graphs are not to scale and are intended to convey a general idea. Answers may vary slightly due to rounding.

9-1.
The null hypothesis is a statistical hypothesis that states there is no difference between a parameter and a specific value or there is no difference between two parameters. The alternative hypothesis specifies a specific difference between a parameter and a specific value, or that there is a difference between two parameters. Examples will vary.

9-3.
A statistical test uses the data obtained from a sample to make a decision as to whether or not the null hypothesis should be rejected.

9-5.
The critical region is the region of values of the test-statistic that indicates a significant difference and the null hypothesis should be rejected. The non-critical region is the region of values of the test-statistic that indicates the difference was probably due to chance, and the null hypothesis should not be rejected.

9-7.
Type I is represented by α, type II is represented by β.

9-9.
A one-tailed test should be used when a specific direction, such as greater than or less than, is being hypothesized, whereas when no direction is specified, a two-tailed test should be used.

9-11.
Hypotheses can only be proved true when the entire population is used to compute the test statistic. In most cases, this is impossible.

9-12.
a. $+2.58, -2.58$

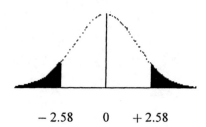

$-2.58 \qquad 0 \qquad +2.58$

b. $+1.65$

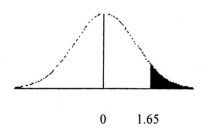

$0 \qquad 1.65$

c. -2.58

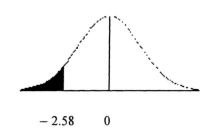

$-2.58 \qquad 0$

d. -1.28

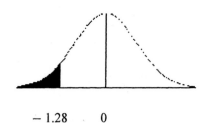

$-1.28 \qquad 0$

e. $+1.96, -1.96$

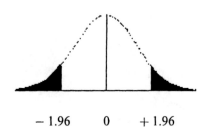

$-1.96 \qquad 0 \qquad +1.96$

9-12. continued

f. + 1.75

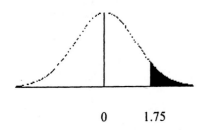

0   1.75

g. − 2.33

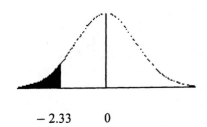

− 2.33   0

h. + 1.65, − 1.65

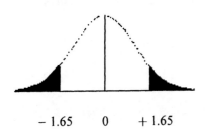

− 1.65   0   + 1.65

i. + 2.05

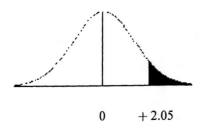

0   + 2.05

j. + 2.33, − 2.33

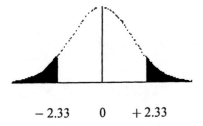

− 2.33   0   + 2.33

9-13.

a. H_0: $\mu = 36.3$ (claim)
       H_1: $\mu \neq 36.3$

b. H_0: $\mu = \$36,250$ (claim)
       H_1: $\mu \neq \$36,250$

c. H_0: $\mu \leq 27.6$ years
       H_1: $\mu > 27.6$ years   (claim)

d. H_0: $\mu \geq 72$
       H_1: $\mu < 72$ (claim)

e. H_0: $\mu \geq 100$
       H_1: $\mu < 100$ (claim)

f. H_0: $\mu = \$297.75$ (claim)
       H_1: $\mu \neq \$297.75$

g. H_0: $\mu \leq \$52.98$
       H_1: $\mu > \$52.98$ (claim)

h. H_0: $\mu \leq 300$ (claim)
       H_1: $\mu > 300$

i. H_0: $\mu \geq 3.6$ (claim)
       H_1: $\mu < 3.6$

9-15.
H_0: $\mu = \$69.21$ (claim)
H_1: $\mu \neq \$69.21$

C. V. $= \pm 1.96$

$z = \dfrac{\overline{X}-\mu}{\frac{\sigma}{\sqrt{n}}} = \dfrac{\$68.43-\$69.21}{\frac{3.72}{\sqrt{30}}} = -1.15$

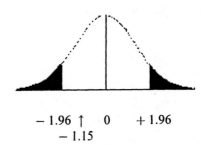

− 1.96 ↑   0   + 1.96
      − 1.15

9-17.
H_0: $\mu \leq \$24$ billion
H1: $\mu > \$24$ billion   (claim)

C. V. $= + 1.65$ $\overline{X} = \$31.5$ s $= \$28.7$

$z = \dfrac{\overline{X}-\mu}{\frac{\sigma}{\sqrt{n}}} = \dfrac{31.5-24}{\frac{28.7}{\sqrt{50}}} = 1.85$

9-17. continued

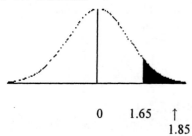

0   1.65   ↑
              1.85

Reject the null hypothesis. There is enough evidence to support the claim that the average revenue exceeds $24 billion.

9-19.
H$_0$: $\mu \geq 14$
H$_1$: $\mu < 14$ (claim)

C. V. $= -2.33$
$z = \frac{\overline{X}-\mu}{\frac{s}{\sqrt{n}}} =$
$\frac{11.8-14}{\frac{2.7}{\sqrt{36}}} = -4.89$

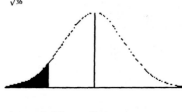

↑ -2.33 0
-4.89

Reject the null hypothesis. There is enough evidence to support the claim that the average age of the planes in the executive's airline is less than the national average.

9-21.
H$_0$: $\mu = \$70$ (claim)
H$_1$: $\mu \neq \$70$

C. V. $= \pm 1.96$ $\overline{X} = 62.4$ $s = 16.1$
$z = \frac{\overline{X}-\mu}{\frac{\sigma}{\sqrt{n}}} = \frac{62.4-70}{\frac{16.1}{\sqrt{30}}} = -2.59$

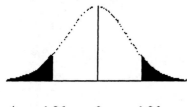

↑ -1.96 0   1.96
-2.59

9-21. continued
Reject the null hypothesis. There is enough evidence to reject the claim that the average age of lottery ticket purchasers is 70.

9-23.
H$_0$: $\mu = 36$ (claim)
H$_1$: $\mu \neq 36$

C. V. $= \pm 2.58$
$z = \frac{\overline{X}-\mu}{\frac{\sigma}{\sqrt{n}}} = \frac{32-36}{\frac{8}{\sqrt{50}}} = -3.54$

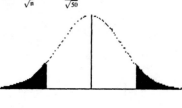

↑ -2.58 0   2.58
-3.54

Reject the null hypothesis. There is enough evidence to reject the claim that the average lifetime of the lightbulbs is 36 months.

9-25.
H$_0$: $\mu \geq 240$
H$_1$: $\mu < 240$

C. V. $= -2.33$
$z = \frac{\overline{X}-\mu}{\frac{\sigma}{\sqrt{n}}} = \frac{229-240}{\frac{18}{\sqrt{40}}} = -3.87$

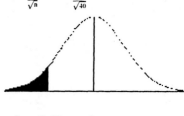

↑ -2.33 0
-3.87

Reject the null hypothesis. There is enough evidence to support the claim that the medication lowers the cholesterol level.

9-27.
H$_0$: $\mu = \$24.44$
H$_1$: $\mu \neq \$24.44$ (claim)

C. V. $= \pm 2.33$
$z = \frac{\overline{X}-\mu}{\frac{s}{\sqrt{n}}} = \frac{22.97-24.44}{\frac{3.70}{\sqrt{33}}} = -2.28$

9-27. continued

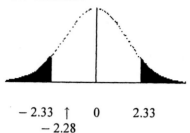

-2.33 ↑   0   2.33
-2.28

Do not reject the null hypothesis. There is
not enough evidence to support the claim
that the amount spent at a local mall is not
equal to the national average of $24.44.

9-29.
a. Do not reject.
b. Do not reject.
c. Do not reject.
d. Reject
e. Reject

9-31.
H_0: $\mu \geq 264$
H_1: $\mu < 264$ (claim)
$z = \frac{\overline{X}-\mu}{\frac{\sigma}{\sqrt{n}}} = \frac{262.3-264}{\frac{3}{\sqrt{20}}} = -2.53$

The area corresponding to z = 2.53 is
0.4943. The P-value is $0.5 - 0.4943 =$
0.0057. The decision is to reject the null
hypothesis since $0.0057 < 0.01$. There is
enough evidence to support the claim that
the average stopping distance is less than
264 feet.

9-33.
H_0: $\mu \leq 84$
H_1: $\mu > 84$ (claim)
$z = \frac{\overline{X}-\mu}{\frac{\sigma}{\sqrt{n}}} = \frac{85.1-84}{\frac{10}{\sqrt{100}}} = 1.1$

The area corresponding to z = 1.1 is 0.3643.
The P-value is $0.5 - 0.3643 =$
0.1357. The decision is do not reject the
null hypothesis since $0.1357 > 0.01$. There
is not enough evidence to support the claim
that the average lifetime of the television
sets is greater than 84 months.

9-35.
H_0: $\mu = 6.32$ (claim)
H_1: $\mu \neq 6.32$
$z = \frac{\overline{X}-\mu}{\frac{\sigma}{\sqrt{n}}} = \frac{6.51-6.32}{\frac{0.54}{\sqrt{50}}} = 2.49$

9-35. continued
The area corresponding to z = 2.49 is
0.4936. To get the P-value, subtract 0.4936
from 0.5 and then multiply by 2 since this is
a two-tailed test.
$2(0.5 - 0.4936) = 2(0.0064) = 0.0128$
The decision is to reject the null hypothesis
since $0.0128 < 0.05$. There is enough
evidence to reject the claim that the average
wage is $6.32.

9-37.
H_0: $\mu = 30,000$ (claim)
H_1: $\mu \neq 30,000$
$z = \frac{\overline{X}-\mu}{\frac{s}{\sqrt{n}}} = \frac{30,456-30,000}{\frac{1684}{\sqrt{40}}} = 1.71$

The area corresponding to z = 1.71 is
0.4564. The P-value is $2(0.5 - 0.4564) =$
$2(0.0436) = 0.0872$.

The decision is to reject the null hypothesis
at $\alpha = 0.10$ since $0.0872 < 0.10$. The
conclusion is that there is enough evidence
to reject the claim that customers are
adhering to the recommendation. A 0.10
significance level is probably appropriate
since there is little consequence of a Type I
error. The dealer would be advised to
increase efforts to make its customers aware
of the service recommendation.

9-39.
H_0: $\mu \geq 10$
H_1: $\mu < 10$ (claim)

$\overline{X} = 5.025$ s = 3.63
$z = \frac{\overline{X}-\mu}{\frac{s}{\sqrt{n}}} = \frac{5.025-10}{\frac{3.63}{\sqrt{40}}} = -8.67$

The area corresponding to 8.67 is 0.4999.
The P-value is $0.5 - 0.499 = 0.001$. Since
$0.001 < 0.05$, the decision is to reject the
null hypothesis. There is enough evidence
to support the claim that the average number
of days missed per year is less than 10.

9-41.

The mean and standard deviation are found as follows:

	f	X_m	$f \cdot X_m$	$f \cdot X_m^2$
8.35 - 8.43	2	8.39	16.78	140.7842
8.44 - 8.52	6	8.48	50.88	431.4624
8.53 - 8.61	12	8.57	102.84	881.3388
8.62 - 8.70	18	8.66	155.88	1349.9208
8.71 - 8.79	10	8.75	87.5	765.625
8.80 - 8.88	2	8.84	17.68	156.2912
	50		431.56	3725.4224

$$\overline{X} = \frac{\Sigma f \cdot X_m}{n} = \frac{431.56}{50} = 8.63$$

$$s = \sqrt{\frac{\Sigma f \cdot X_m^2 - \frac{\Sigma (f \cdot X_m)^2}{n}}{n-1}} = \sqrt{\frac{3725.4224 - \frac{(431.56)^2}{50}}{49}}$$

$$= 0.105$$

H_0: $\mu = 8.65$ (claim)
H_1: $\mu \neq 8.65$

C. V. $= \pm 1.96$

$$z = \frac{\overline{X} - \mu}{\frac{s}{\sqrt{n}}} = \frac{8.63 - 8.65}{\frac{0.105}{\sqrt{50}}} = -1.35$$

Do not reject the null hypothesis. There is not enough evidence to reject the claim that the average hourly wage of the employees is $8.65.

9-43.

The degrees of freedom are the number of values that are free to vary after a sample statistic has been computed. They tell the researcher which specific curve to use when a distribution consists of a family of curves.

9-45.

a. d. f. $= 9$ C. V. $= +1.833$
b. d. f. $= 17$ C. V. $= \pm 1.740$
c. d. f. $= 5$ C. V. $= -3.365$
d. d. f. $= 8$ C. V. $= +2.306$
e. d. f. $= 14$ C. V. $= \pm 2.145$
f. d. f. $= 22$ C. V. $= -2.819$
g. d. f. $= 27$ C. V. $= \pm 2.771$
h. d. f. $= 16$ C. V. $= \pm 2.583$

9-46.

Specific P-values are in parentheses.
a. $0.01 < $ P-value < 0.025 (0.018)
b. $0.05 < $ P-value < 0.10 (0.062)
c. $0.10 < $ P-value < 0.25 (0.123)
d. $0.10 < $ P-value < 0.20 (0.138)

9-46. continued

e. P-value < 0.005 (0.003)
f. $0.10 < $ P-value < 0.25 (0.158)
g. P-value $= 0.05$ (0.05)
h. P-value > 0.25 (0.261)

9-47.

H_0: $\mu \geq 11.52$
H_1: $\mu < 11.52$ (claim)

C. V. $= -1.833$ d. f. $= 6$

$$t = \frac{\overline{X} - \mu}{\frac{s}{\sqrt{n}}} = \frac{7.42 - 11.52}{\frac{1.3}{\sqrt{10}}} = -9.97$$

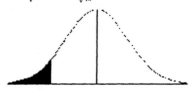

↑ -1.833 0
-9.97

Reject the null hypothesis. There is enough evidence to support the claim that the rainfall is below average.

9-49.

H_0: $\mu = 800$ (claim)
H_1: $\mu \neq 800$

C. V. $= \pm 2.262$ d. f. $= 9$

$$t = \frac{\overline{X} - \mu}{\frac{s}{\sqrt{n}}} = \frac{863 - 800}{\frac{20}{\sqrt{10}}} = 9.96$$

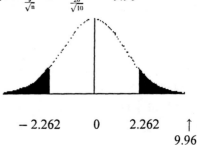

-2.262 0   2.262   ↑
                                9.96

Reject the null hypothesis. There is enough evidence to reject the claim that the average rent that small-business establishments pay in Eagle City is $800.

9-51.

H_0: $\mu \geq 700$ (claim)
H_1: $\mu < 700$
$\overline{X} = 606.5$ $s = 109.1$
C. V. $= -2.262$ d. f. $= 9$

$$t = \frac{\overline{X} - \mu}{\frac{s}{\sqrt{n}}} = \frac{606.5 - 700}{\frac{109.1}{\sqrt{10}}} = -2.71$$

9-51. continued

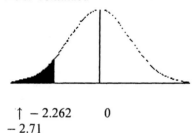

$\uparrow -2.262 \qquad 0$
-2.71

Reject the null hypothesis. There is enough evidence to reject the claim that the average height of the buildings is at least 700 feet.

9-53.
$H_0: \mu = \$750$ (claim)
$H_1: \mu \neq \$750$

C. V. $= \pm 3.106$ $\qquad$ d. f. $= 11$
$t = \frac{\overline{X}-\mu}{\frac{s}{\sqrt{n}}} = \frac{732-750}{\frac{17}{\sqrt{12}}} = -3.67$

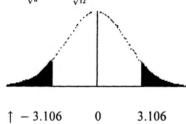

$\uparrow -3.106 \qquad 0 \qquad 3.106$
-3.67

Reject the null hypothesis. There is enough evidence to reject the claim that the average rent is $750.

9-55.
$H_0: \mu \leq 350$
$H_1: \mu > 350$ (claim)

C. V. $= +1.796$ $\qquad$ d. f. $= 11$
$t = \frac{\overline{X}-\mu}{\frac{s}{\sqrt{n}}} = \frac{358-350}{\frac{16}{\sqrt{12}}} = 1.796$

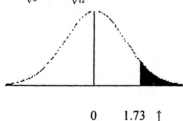

$0 \qquad 1.73 \;\uparrow$
$\qquad\qquad 1.796$

Do not reject the null hypothesis. There is not enough evidence to support the claim that the average fine is higher than $350.

9-57.
$H_0: \mu \geq 37$ (claim)
$H_1: \mu < 37$
d. f. $= 28$
$0.025 < $P-value$ < 0.05$ (0.035)
$t = \frac{\overline{X}-\mu}{\frac{s}{\sqrt{n}}} = \frac{34.9-37}{\frac{6}{\sqrt{29}}} = -1.89$

Since P-value < 0.05, reject the null hypothesis. There is enough evidence to reject the claim that the average household receives at least 37 phone calls per month.

9-59.
$H_0: \mu = 75$ (claim)
$H_1: \mu \neq 75$
$\overline{X} = 70.85 \qquad s = 6.56$
d. f. $= 19$
$0.01 < $P-value$ < 0.02$ (0.011)
$t = \frac{\overline{X}-\mu}{\frac{s}{\sqrt{n}}} = \frac{70.85-75}{\frac{6.56}{\sqrt{20}}} = -2.83$

Since P-value > 0.01, do not reject the null hypothesis. There is not enough evidence to reject the claim that the average score on the real estate exam is 75.

9-61.
Answers will vary.

9-63.
$np \geq 5$ and $nq \geq 5$

9-65.
$H_0: p \geq 0.23$ (claim)
$H_1: p < 0.23$

$\hat{p} = \frac{7}{40} = 0.175 \qquad p = 0.23 \qquad q = 0.77$
C. V. $= -1.65$

$z = \frac{\hat{p}-p}{\sqrt{\frac{pq}{n}}} = \frac{0.175-0.23}{\sqrt{\frac{(0.23)(0.77)}{40}}} = -0.83$

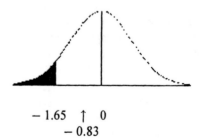

$-1.65 \;\uparrow\; 0$
$\qquad -0.83$

Do not reject the null hypothesis. There is not enough evidence to reject the claim that

9-65. continued
at least 23% of the 14 year old residents own
a skateboard.

9-67.
H_0: $p \geq 0.40$ (claim)
H_1: $p < 0.40$

$\hat{p} = \frac{30}{80} = 0.375$ $p = 0.40$ $q = 0.60$
C. V. $= -1.28$
$z = \frac{\hat{p}-p}{\sqrt{\frac{pq}{n}}} = \frac{0.375-0.40}{\sqrt{\frac{(0.40)(0.60)}{80}}} = -0.457$

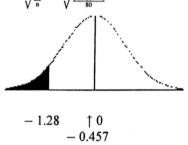

-1.28 $\uparrow 0$
-0.457

Do not reject the null hypothesis. There is
not enough evidence to reject the claim that
at least 40% of the arsonists are under 21.

9-69.
H_0: $p = 0.63$ (claim)
H_1: $p \neq 0.63$

$\hat{p} = \frac{85}{143} = 0.5944$ $p = 0.63$ $q = 0.37$
C. V. $= \pm 1.96$
$z = \frac{\hat{p}-p}{\sqrt{\frac{pq}{n}}} = \frac{0.5944-0.63}{\sqrt{\frac{(0.63)(0.37)}{143}}} = -0.88$

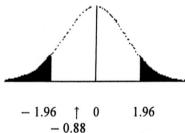

-1.96 $\uparrow 0$ 1.96
-0.88

Do not reject the null hypothesis. There is
not enough evidence to reject the claim that
the percentage is the same.

9-71.
H_0: $p \geq 0.15$ (claim)
H_1: $p < 0.15$

$\hat{p} = \frac{9}{80} = 0.1125$ $p = 0.15$ $q = 0.85$
C. V. $= -1.65$
$z = \frac{\hat{p}-p}{\sqrt{\frac{pq}{n}}} = \frac{0.1125-0.15}{\sqrt{\frac{(0.15)(0.85)}{80}}} = -0.94$

9-71. continued

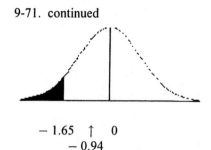

-1.65 $\uparrow$ 0
-0.94

Do not reject the null hypothesis. There is
not enough evidence to reject the claim that
at least 15% of all eighth-grade students are
overweight.

9-73.
H_0: $p \leq 0.30$
H_1: $p > 0.30$ (claim)

$\hat{p} = \frac{72}{200} = 0.36$ $p = 0.30$ $q = 0.70$
$z = \frac{\hat{p}-p}{\sqrt{\frac{pq}{n}}} = \frac{0.36-0.30}{\sqrt{\frac{(0.30)(0.70)}{200}}} = 1.85$
Area $= 0.4678$
P-value $= 0.5 - 0.4678 = 0.0322$
Since P-value ≤ 0.05, reject the null
hypothesis. There is enough evidence to
support the claim that more than 30% of the
customers have at least two telephones.

9-75.
H_0: $p = 0.18$ (claim)
H_1: $p \neq 0.18$

$\hat{p} = \frac{50}{300} = 0.1667$ $p = 0.18$ $q = 0.82$
$z = \frac{\hat{p}-p}{\sqrt{\frac{pq}{n}}} = \frac{0.1667-0.18}{\sqrt{\frac{(0.18)(0.82)}{300}}} = -0.60$
Area $= 0.2257$
P-value $= 2(0.5 - 0.2257) = 0.5486$
Since P-value > 0.01, do not reject the null
hypothesis. There is not enough evidence to
reject the claim that 18% of all high school
students smoke at least a pack of cigarettes a
day.

9-77.
Using the binomial distribution, $P(X = 5,$
$p = 0.2, n = 15) = 0.103$. Since
$0.103 > \frac{0.10}{2}$ or 0.05, there is not enough
evidence to indicate that the 20% estimate
has changed.

9-79.
a. H_0: $\sigma^2 \leq 225$
   H_1: $\sigma^2 > 225$

9-79. continued
C. V. = 27.587   d. f. = 17

0   27.587

b. H_0: $\sigma^2 \geq 225$
    H_1: $\sigma^2 < 225$

C. V. = 14.042   d. f. = 22

0   14.042

c. H_0: $\sigma^2 = 225$
    H_1: $\sigma^2 \neq 225$

C. V. = 5.629, 26.119   d. f. = 14

0   5.629   26.119

d. H_0: $\sigma^2 = 225$
    H_1: $\sigma^2 \neq 225$

C. V. = 2.167, 14.067   d. f. = 7

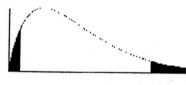

0   2.167   14.067

e. H_0: $\sigma^2 \leq 225$
    H_1: $\sigma^2 > 225$

C. V. = 32.000   d. f. = 16

9-79. continued

0   32.000

f. H_0: $\sigma^2 \geq 225$
    H_1: $\sigma^2 < 225$

C. V. = 8.907   d. f. = 19

0   8.907

g. H_0: $\sigma^2 = 225$
    H_1: $\sigma^2 \neq 225$

C. V. = 3.074, 28.299   d. f. = 12

0   3.074   28.299

h. H_0: $\sigma^2 \geq 225$
    H_1: $\sigma^2 < 225$

C. V. = 15.308   d. f. = 28

0   15.308

9-80.
a. 0.01 < P-value < 0.025   (0.015)
b. 0.005 < P-value < 0.01   (0.006)
c. 0.01 < P-value < 0.025   (0.012)
d. P-value < 0.005   (0.003)
e. 0.025 < P-value < 0.05   (0.037)
f. 0.10 < P-value < 0.20   (0.088)
g. 0.05 < P-value < 0.10   (0.066)

9-80. continued

h. P-value < 0.01   (0.007)

9-81.

H_0: $\sigma = 60$ (claim)
H_1: $\sigma \neq 60$

C. V. = 8.672, 27.587 $\alpha = 0.10$
d. f. = 17
s = 64.6
$\chi^2 = \frac{(n-1)s^2}{\sigma^2} = \frac{(18-1)(64.6)^2}{(60)^2} = 19.707$

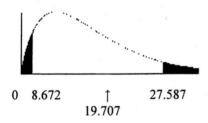

0   8.672   ↑   27.587
                 19.707

Do not reject the null hypothesis. There is not enough evidence to reject the claim that the standard deviation is 60.

9-83.

H_0: $\sigma^2 \leq 25$ (claim)
H_1: $\sigma^2 > 25$

C. V. = 27.204 $\alpha = 0.10$ d. f. = 19

$\chi^2 = \frac{(n-1)s^2}{\sigma^2} = \frac{(20-1)(36)}{25} = 27.36$

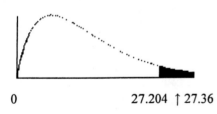

0   27.204 ↑ 27.36

Reject the null hypothesis. There is enough evidence to reject the claim that the variance is less than or equal to 25.

9-85.

H_0: $\sigma \leq 1.2$ (claim)
H_1: $\sigma > 1.2$

$\alpha = 0.01$ d. f. = 14
$\chi^2 = \frac{(n-1)s^2}{\sigma^2} = \frac{(15-1)(1.8)^2}{(1.2)^2} = 31.5$
P-value < 0.005   (0.0047)

9-85. continued

Since P-value < 0.01, reject the null hypothesis. There is enough evidence to reject the claim that the standard deviation is less than or equal to 1.2 minutes.

9-87.

H_0: $\sigma \leq 2$
H_1: $\sigma > 2$ (claim)

C. V. = 24.725 $\alpha = 0.01$ d. f. = 11
$\chi^2 = \frac{(n-1)s^2}{\sigma^2} = \frac{((12-1)(2.83)^2}{2^2} = 22.02$

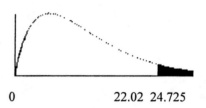

0   22.02 24.725

Do not reject the null hypothesis. The lot is acceptable, since there is not enough evidence to support the claim that the standard deviation is greater than 2 pounds.

9-89.

H_0: $\mu = 1800$ (claim)
H_1: $\mu \neq 1800$

C. V. = ± 1.96

$z = \frac{\overline{X}-\mu}{\frac{\sigma}{\sqrt{n}}} = \frac{1830-1800}{\frac{200}{\sqrt{10}}} = 0.47$

− 1.96   0   ↑   1.96
               0.47

The 95% confidence interval of the mean is:
$\overline{X} - z_{\frac{\alpha}{2}}\frac{\sigma}{\sqrt{n}} < \mu < \overline{X} + z_{\frac{\alpha}{2}}\frac{\sigma}{\sqrt{n}}$

$1830 - 1.96\left(\frac{200}{\sqrt{10}}\right) < \mu <$
$\qquad\qquad 1830 + 1.96\left(\frac{200}{\sqrt{10}}\right)$

$1706.04 < \mu < 1953.96$

The hypothesized mean is within the interval, thus we can be 95% confident that the average sales will be between $1706.94 and $1953.96.

9-91.

$H_0: \mu = 86$ (claim)

$H_1: \mu \neq 86$

C. V. $= \pm 2.58$

$z = \dfrac{\overline{X}-\mu}{\frac{\sigma}{\sqrt{n}}} = \dfrac{84-86}{\frac{6}{\sqrt{15}}} = -1.29$

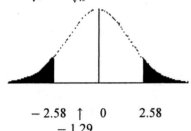

$\quad -2.58 \uparrow \quad 0 \qquad 2.58$

$\qquad\quad -1.29$

$\overline{X} - z_{\frac{\alpha}{2}} \dfrac{\sigma}{\sqrt{n}} < \mu < \overline{X} + z_{\frac{\alpha}{2}} \dfrac{\sigma}{\sqrt{n}}$

$84 - 2.58 \cdot \dfrac{6}{\sqrt{15}} < \mu < 84 + 1.58 \cdot \dfrac{6}{\sqrt{15}}$

$80.00 < \mu < 88.00$

The decision is do not reject the null hypothesis since $-1.29 > -2.58$ and the 99% confidence interval contains the hypothesized mean. There is not enough evidence to reject the claim that the monthly maintenance is $86.

9-93.

$H_0: \mu = 22$

$H_1: \mu \neq 22$ (claim)

C. V. $= \pm 2.58$

$z = \dfrac{\overline{X}-\mu}{\frac{\sigma}{\sqrt{n}}} = \dfrac{20.8-22}{\frac{4}{\sqrt{60}}} = -2.32$

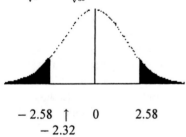

$\quad -2.58 \uparrow \quad 0 \qquad 2.58$

$\qquad\quad -2.32$

The 99% confidence interval of the mean is:

$\overline{X} - z_{\frac{\alpha}{2}} \dfrac{\sigma}{\sqrt{n}} < \mu < \overline{X} + z_{\frac{\alpha}{2}} \dfrac{\sigma}{\sqrt{n}}$

$20.8 - 2.58 \cdot \dfrac{4}{\sqrt{60}} < \mu < 20.8 + 2.58 \cdot \dfrac{4}{\sqrt{60}}$

$19.47 < \mu < 22.13$

9-93. continued

The decision is do not reject the null hypothesis since $-2.32 > -2.58$ and the 99% confidence interval does contain the hypothesized mean of 22. The conclusion is that there is not enough evidence to support the claim that the average studying time has changed.

9-95.

$H_0: \mu = 98°$ (claim)

$H_1: \mu \neq 98°$

C. V. $= \pm 1.96$

$z = \dfrac{\overline{X}-\mu}{\frac{s}{\sqrt{n}}} = \dfrac{95.8-98}{\frac{7.71}{\sqrt{50}}} = -2.02$

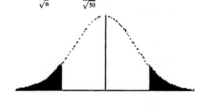

$\uparrow \quad -1.96 \qquad 0 \qquad 1.96$

-2.02

Reject the null hypothesis. There is enough evidence to reject the claim that the average high temperature is 98°.

9-97.

$H_0: \mu = 16.3$ (claim)

$H_1: \mu \neq 16.3$

$z = \dfrac{\overline{X}-\mu}{\frac{\sigma}{\sqrt{n}}} = \dfrac{16.9-16.3}{\frac{0.3}{\sqrt{32}}} = 11.3$

Area $= 0.4999$

P-value $= 2(.5 - 0.4999) = 0.0002$

Since P-value < 0.01, reject the null hypothesis. There is enough evidence to reject the claim that the average age is 16.3.

9-99.

$H_0: \mu \leq 67$

$H_1: \mu > 67$ (claim)

C. V. $= 1.383$ d. f. $= 9$

$t = \dfrac{\overline{X}-\mu}{\frac{s}{\sqrt{n}}} = \dfrac{69.6-67.0}{\frac{1.1}{\sqrt{10}}} = 7.47$

9-99. continued

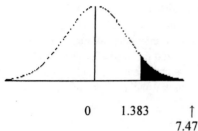

$$0 \qquad 1.383 \qquad \underset{7.47}{\uparrow}$$

Reject the null hypothesis. There is enough evidence to support the claim that 1995 was warmer than average.

9-101.
H_0: $\mu = 6$ (claim)
H_1: $\mu \neq 6$

C. V. = ± 2.821 $\quad \overline{X} = 8.42$ $\quad s = 4.17$
$t = \frac{\overline{X}-\mu}{\frac{s}{\sqrt{n}}} = \frac{8.42-6}{\frac{4.17}{\sqrt{10}}} = 1.835$

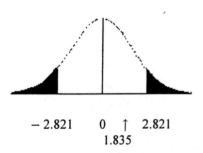

$$-2.821 \qquad 0 \;\uparrow\; 2.821$$
$$1.835$$

Do not reject the null hypothesis. There is not enough evidence to support the claim that the average attendance has changed.

9-103.
H_0: $p \geq 0.60$ (claim)
H_1: $p < 0.60$

C. V. = -1.28
$\hat{p} = 0.54$ $\quad p = 0.60$ $\quad q = 0.40$
$z = \frac{\hat{p}-p}{\sqrt{\frac{pq}{n}}} = \frac{0.54-0.6}{\sqrt{\frac{(0.6)(0.4)}{100}}} = -1.22$

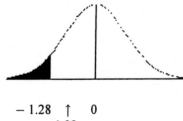

$$-1.28 \;\uparrow\; 0$$
$$-1.22$$

Do not reject the null hypothesis. There is not enough evidence to reject the claim that

9-103. continued
at least 60% of adults eat eggs for breakfast at least four times per week.

9-105.
H_0: $p = 0.65$ (claim)
H_1: $p \neq 0.65$

$\hat{p} = \frac{57}{80} = 0.7125$ $\quad p = 0.65$ $\quad q = 0.35$
$z = \frac{\hat{p}-p}{\sqrt{\frac{pq}{n}}} = \frac{0.7125-0.65}{\sqrt{\frac{(0.65)(0.35)}{80}}} = 1.17$

Area = 0.3790
P-value = $2(0.5 - 0.3790) = 0.242$
Since P-value > 0.05, do not reject the null hypothesis. There is not enough evidence to reject the claim that 65% of the teenagers own their own radios.

9-107.
H_0: $\mu \geq 10$
H_1: $\mu < 10$ (claim)

$z = \frac{\overline{X}-\mu}{\frac{\sigma}{\sqrt{n}}} = \frac{9.25-10}{\frac{2}{\sqrt{25}}} = -1.88$

Area = 0.4699
P-value = $0.5 - 0.4699 = 0.0301$
Since $0.0301 < 0.05$, reject the null hypothesis. The conclusion is that there is enough evidence to support the claim that the average time is less than 10 minutes.

9-109.
H_0: $\sigma \geq 4.3$ (claim)
H_1: $\sigma < 4.3$

d. f. = 19
$\chi^2 = \frac{(n-1)s^2}{\sigma^2} = \frac{(20-1)(2.6)^2}{(4.3)^2} = 6.95$

$0.005 < $ P-value $ < 0.01$ (0.006)
Since P-value < 0.05, reject the null hypothesis. There is enough evidence to reject the claim that the standard deviation is greater than or equal to 4.3 miles per gallon.

9-111.
H_0: $\sigma = 18$ (claim)
H_1: $\sigma \neq 18$

C. V. = 11.143 and 0.484 $\quad$ d. f. = 4

$\chi^2 = \frac{(n-1)s^2}{\sigma^2} = \frac{(5-1)(21)^2}{18^2} = 5.44$

9-111. continued

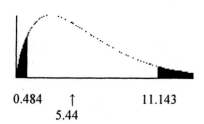

0.484   ↑   11.143
       5.44

Do not reject the null hypothesis. There is not enough evidence to reject the claim that the standard deviation is 21 minutes.

9-113.
H_0: $\mu = 4$
H_1: $\mu \neq 4$ (claim)

C. V. $= \pm 2.58$
$z = \dfrac{\overline{X} - \mu}{\frac{s}{\sqrt{n}}} = \dfrac{4.2 - 4}{\frac{0.6}{\sqrt{20}}} = 1.49$

The 99% confidence interval of the mean is:

$$\overline{X} - z_{\frac{\alpha}{2}}\frac{\sigma}{\sqrt{n}} < \mu < \overline{X} + z_{\frac{\alpha}{2}}\frac{\sigma}{\sqrt{n}}$$

$4.2 - 2.58 \cdot \dfrac{0.6}{\sqrt{20}} < \mu < 4.2 + 2.58 \cdot \dfrac{0.6}{\sqrt{20}}$
$3.85 < \mu < 4.55$

The decision is do not reject the null hypothesis since $1.49 < 2.58$ and the confidence interval does contain the hypothesized mean of 4. There is not enough evidence to support the claim that the growth has changed.

Quiz
1. False, it is an example of a type I error.
2. True
3. False, the critical value separates the critical region from the noncritical region.
4. True
5. False, it can be one-tailed or two-tailed.
6. b
7. d
8. c
9. b
10. type I
11. β
12. statistical hypothesis
13. right
14. $n - 1$

15. H_0: $\mu = 28.6$ (claim)
H_1: $\mu \neq 28.6$
C. V. $= \pm 1.96$
$z = 2.09$
Reject the null hypothesis. There is enough evidence to reject the claim that the average age is 28.6.

16. H_0: $\mu = \$6,500$ (claim)
H_1: $\mu \neq \$6,500$
C. V. $= \pm 1.96$
$z = 5.27$
Reject the null hypothesis. There is enough evidence to reject the agent's claim.

17. H_0: $\mu \leq 8$
H_1: $\mu > 8$ (claim)
C. V. $= 1.65$
$z = 6.00$
Reject the null hypothesis. There is enough evidence to support the claim that the average number of sticks is greater than 8.

18. H_0: $\mu = 21$ (claim)
H_1: $\mu \neq 21$
C. V. $= \pm 2.921$
$t = -2.06$
Do not reject the null hypothesis. There is not enough evidence to reject the claim that the average number of dropouts is 21.

19. H_0: $\mu \geq 67$
H_1: $\mu < 67$ (claim)
$t = -3.1568$
P-value < 0.005 (0.003)
Since P-value < 0.05, reject the null hypothesis. There is enough evidence to support the claim that the average height is less than 67 inches.

20. H_0: $\mu \geq 12.4$
H_1: $\mu < 12.4$ (claim)
C. V. $= -1.345$
$t = -0.328$
Reject the null hypothesis. There is enough evidence to support the claim that the average is less than what the company claimed.

21. H_0: $\mu \leq 63.5$
H_1: $\mu > 63.5$ (claim)
$t = 0.47$
P-value > 0.25 (0.322)
Since P-value > 0.05, do not reject the null hypothesis. There is not enough evidence to

21. continued
support the claim that the average is greater than 63.5.

22. H_0: $\mu = 26$ (claim)
H_1: $\mu \neq 26$
C. V. = ± 2.492
t = -1.5
Do not reject the null hypothesis. There is not enough evidence to reject the claim that the average age is 26.

23. H_0: p ≥ 0.25 (claim)
H_1: p < 0.25
$\mu = 25$ $\sigma = 4.33$
C. V. = -1.65
z = -0.69
Do not reject the null hypothesis. There is not enough evidence to reject the claim that the proportion is at least 0.25.

24. H_0: p ≥ 0.55 (claim)
H_1: p < 0.55
$\mu = 44$ $\sigma = 4.45$
C. V. = -1.28
z = -0.899
Do not reject the null hypothesis. There is not enough evidence to reject the dietitian's claim.

25. H_0: p $= 0.7$ (claim)
H_1: p $\neq 0.7$
$\mu = 21$ $\sigma = 2.51$
C. V. = ± 2.33
z = 0.797
Do not reject the null hypothesis. There is not enough evidence to reject the claim that the proportion is 0.7.

26. H_0: p $= 0.75$ (claim)
H_1: p $\neq 0.75$
$\mu = 45$ $\sigma = 3.35$
C. V. = ± 2.58
z = 2.68
Reject the null hypothesis. there is enough evidence to reject the claim.

27. The area corresponding to z $= 2.09$ is 0.4817. P-
value $= 2(0.5 - 0.4817) = 0.036$.

28. The area corresponding to z $= 5.27$ is more than 0.4999. Hence, the P-value is less than 0.0001.

29. H_0: $\sigma \leq 6$
H_1: $\sigma > 6$ (claim)
C. V. = 36.415
$\chi^2 = 54$
Reject the null hypothesis. There is enough evidence to support the claim that the standard deviation is 6 pages.

30. H_0: $\sigma = 8$ (claim)
H_1: $\sigma \neq 8$
C. V. = 27.991, 79.490
$\chi^2 = 33.2$
Do not reject the null hypothesis. There is not enough evidence to reject the claim that $\sigma = 8$.

31. H_0: $\sigma \geq 2.3$
H_1: $\sigma < 2.3$ (claim)
C. V. = 10.117
$\chi^2 = 13$
Reject the null hypothesis. There is enough evidence to support the claim that the standard deviation is less than 2.3.

32. H_0: $\sigma = 9$ (claim)
H_1: $\sigma \neq 9$
$\chi^2 = 13.4$
P-value > 0.20 (0.291)
Since P-value > 0.05, do not reject the null hypothesis. There is not enough evidence to reject the claim that $\sigma = 9$.

33. $28.7 < \mu < 31.4$

34. $\$6562.81 < \mu < \$6,637.19$

Chapter 10 - Testing the Difference
Between Two Means, Two Variances, and Two Proportions

Note: Graphs are not to scale and are intended to convey a general idea. Answers may vary slightly due to rounding.

10-1.
Testing a single mean involves comparing a sample mean to a specific value such as $\mu = 100$; whereas testing the difference between means means comparing the means of two samples such as $\mu_1 = \mu_2$.

10-3.
The populations must be independent of each other and they must be normally distributed. s_1 and s_2 can be used in place of σ_1 and σ_2 when σ_1 and σ_2 are unknown and both samples are each greater than or equal to 30.

10-5.
$H_0: \mu_1 = \mu_2$ (claim)
$H_1: \mu_1 \neq \mu_2$

C. V. $= \pm 2.58$

$\overline{X}_1 = 662.6111$ $\overline{X}_2 = 758.875$
$s_1 = 449.8703$ $s_2 = 474.1258$

$z = \dfrac{(\overline{X}_1 - \overline{X}_2) - (\mu_1 - \mu_2)}{\sqrt{\frac{\sigma_1^2}{n_1} + \frac{\sigma_2^2}{n_2}}} = \dfrac{(662.6111 - 758.875) - 0}{\sqrt{\frac{449.8703^2}{36} + \frac{474.1258^2}{32}}} =$
$z = -0.856$

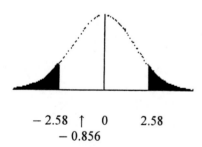

-2.58 $\uparrow$ 0 2.58
     -0.856

Do not reject the null hypothesis. There is not enough evidence to reject the claim that the average lengths of the rivers is the same.

10-7.
$H_0: \mu_1 \leq \mu_2$
$H_1: \mu_1 > \mu_2$ (claim)

C. V. $= 1.65$

$z = \dfrac{(\overline{X}_1 - \overline{X}_2) - (\mu_1 - \mu_2)}{\sqrt{\frac{s_1^2}{n_1} + \frac{s_2^2}{n_2}}} = \dfrac{(90 - 88) - 0}{\sqrt{\frac{5^2}{100} + \frac{6^2}{100}}} = 2.56$

10-7. continued

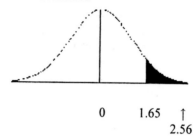

0 1.65 $\uparrow$
            2.56

Reject the null hypothesis. There is enough evidence to support the claim that pulse rates of smokers are higher than the pulse rates of non-smokers.

10-9.
$H_0: \mu_1 \leq \mu_2$
$H_1: \mu_1 > \mu_2$ (claim)
C. V. $= 2.05$

$z = \dfrac{(\overline{X}_1 - \overline{X}_2) - (\mu_1 - \mu_2)}{\sqrt{\frac{s_1^2}{n_1} + \frac{s_2^2}{n_2}}} = \dfrac{(61.2 - 59.4) - 0}{\sqrt{\frac{7.9^2}{84} + \frac{7.9^2}{34}}} = 1.12$

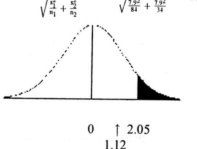

0 $\uparrow$ 2.05
   1.12

Do not reject the null hypothesis. There is not enough evidence to support the claim that noise levels in the corridors is higher than in the clinics.

10-11.
$H_0: \mu_1 \geq \mu_2$
$H_1: \mu_1 < \mu_2$ (claim)
C. V. $= -1.65$

$z = \dfrac{(\overline{X}_1 - \overline{X}_2) - (\mu_1 - \mu_2)}{\sqrt{\frac{s_1^2}{n_1} + \frac{s_2^2}{n_2}}} = \dfrac{(3.16 - 3.28) - 0}{\sqrt{\frac{0.52^2}{103} + \frac{0.46^2}{225}}} = -2.01$

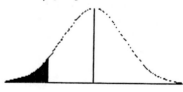

$\uparrow$ -1.65 0
-2.01

10-11. continued
Reject the null hypothesis. There is enough evidence to support the claim that leavers have a lower GPA than stayers.

10-13.
H_0: $\mu_1 \leq \mu_2$
H_1: $\mu_1 > \mu_2$ (claim)

C. V. = 2.33
$\overline{X}_1 = \$9224$ $\overline{X}_2 = \$8497.5$
$s_1 = 3829.826$ $s_2 = 2745.293$

$$z = \frac{(\overline{X}_1 - \overline{X}_2) - (\mu_1 - \mu_2)}{\sqrt{\frac{s_1^2}{n_1} + \frac{s_2^2}{n_2}}}$$

$$z = \frac{(9224 - 8497.5) - 0}{\sqrt{\frac{3829.826^2}{50} + \frac{2745.293^2}{50}}} = 1.09$$

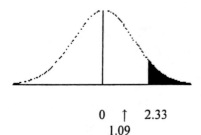

0   ↑   2.33
1.09

Do not reject the null hypothesis. There is not enough evidence to support the claim that colleges spent more money on men's sports than women's.

10-15.
H_0: $\mu_1 = \mu_2$
H_1: $\mu_1 \neq \mu_2$ (claim)

$$z = \frac{(\overline{X}_1 - \overline{X}_2) - (\mu_1 - \mu_2)}{\sqrt{\frac{s_1^2}{n_1} + \frac{s_2^2}{n_2}}} = \frac{(3.05 - 2.96) - 0}{\sqrt{\frac{0.75^2}{103} + \frac{0.75^2}{225}}}$$

$z = 1.01$
Area = 0.3438
P-value = 2(0.5 - 0.3438) = 0.3124
Since P-value > 0.05, do not reject the null hypothesis. There is not enough evidence to support the claim that there is a difference in self-esteem scores.

10-17.
$\overline{D} = 83.6 - 79.2 = 4.4$

10-17. continued
$$(\overline{X}_1 - \overline{X}_2) - z_{\frac{\alpha}{2}} \sqrt{\frac{\sigma_1^2}{n_1} + \frac{\sigma_2^2}{n_2}} < \mu_1 - \mu_2 <$$
$$(\overline{X}_1 - \overline{X}_2) + z_{\frac{\alpha}{2}} \sqrt{\frac{\sigma_1^2}{n_1} + \frac{\sigma_2^2}{n_2}}$$

$$4.4 - (1.65)\sqrt{\frac{4.3^2}{36} + \frac{3.8^2}{36}} < \mu_1 - \mu_2 <$$
$$4.4 + (1.65)\sqrt{\frac{4.3^2}{36} + \frac{3.8^2}{36}}$$

$$2.82 < \mu_1 - \mu_2 < 5.98$$

10-19.
$\overline{D} = 28.6 - 32.9 = -4.3$

$$(\overline{X}_1 - \overline{X}_2) - z_{\frac{\alpha}{2}} \sqrt{\frac{\sigma_1^2}{n_1} + \frac{\sigma_2^2}{n_2}} < \mu_1 - \mu_2 <$$
$$(\overline{X}_1 - \overline{X}_2) + z_{\frac{\alpha}{2}} \sqrt{\frac{\sigma_1^2}{n_1} + \frac{\sigma_2^2}{n_2}}$$

$$-4.3 - (2.58)\sqrt{\frac{5.1^2}{30} + \frac{4.4^2}{40}} < \mu_1 - \mu_2 <$$
$$-4.3 + (2.58)\sqrt{\frac{5.2^2}{30} + \frac{4.4^2}{40}}$$

$$-7.3 < \mu_1 - \mu_2 < -1.3$$

10-21.
H_0: $\mu_1 - \mu_2 \leq 8$ (claim)
H_1: $\mu_1 - \mu_2 > 8$

C. V. = 1.65

$$z = \frac{(\overline{X}_1 - \overline{X}_2) - K}{\sqrt{\frac{s_1^2}{n_1} + \frac{s_2^2}{n_2}}} = \frac{(110 - 104) - 8}{\sqrt{\frac{15^2}{60} + \frac{15^2}{60}}} = -0.73$$

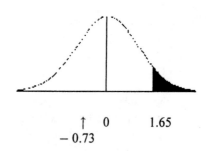

↑   0   1.65
-0.73

Do not reject the null hypothesis. There is not enough evidence to reject the claim that private school students have exam scores that are at most 8 points higher than public school students.

Chapter 10 - Testing the Difference
Between Two Means, Two Variances, and Two Proportions

10-23.
The critical region is on the right side because the F test value is always greater than or equal to 1, since the larger variance is always placed in the numerator.

10-25.
One d.f. is used for the variance associated with the numerator and one is used for the variance associated with the denominator.

10-27.
a. d. f. N = 15, d. f. D = 22; C. V. = 3.36
b. d. f. N = 24, d. f. D = 13; C. V. = 3.59
c. d. f. N = 45, d. f. D = 29; C. V. = 2.03
d. d. f. N = 20, d. f. D = 16; C. V. = 2.28
e. d. f. N = 10, d. f. D = 10; C. V. = 2.98

10-28.
Note: Specific P-values are in parentheses.
a. $0.025 < $ P-value < 0.05 (0.033)
b. $0.10 < $ P-value < 0.05 (0.072)
c. P-value $= 0.05$
d. $0.005 < $ P-value < 0.01 (0.006)
e. P-value $= 0.05$
f. $P > 0.10$ (0.112)
g. $0.05 < $ P-value < 0.10 (0.068)
h. $0.01 < $ P-value < 0.02 (0.015)

10-29.
H_0: $\sigma_1^2 \leq \sigma_2^2$ (claim)

H_1: $\sigma_1^2 > \sigma_2^2$

C. V. = 2.23 $\alpha = 0.05$
d. f. N = 19   d. f. D = 19

$F = \frac{s_1^2}{s_2^2} = \frac{103}{73} = 1.41$

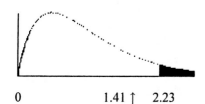

0   1.41 ↑   2.23

Do not reject the null hypothesis. There is not enough evidence to support the claim that variance of the exam scores of the students who had the word processing will be larger than the variance of the exam scores of the students who did not have the

10-29. continued
word processing in conjunction with a composition course.

10-31.
H_0: $\sigma_1^2 = \sigma_2^2$

H_1: $\sigma_1^2 \neq \sigma_2^2$ (claim)

$s_1 = 25.97$ $s_2 = 72.74$
C. V. = 2.86 $\alpha = 0.05$
d. f. N = 15   d. f. D = 15

$F = \frac{s_1^2}{s_2^2} = \frac{72.74^2}{25.97^2} = 7.85$

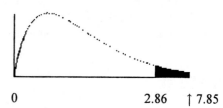

0   2.86   ↑ 7.85

Reject the null hypothesis. There is enough evidence to support the claim that the variances of the values of tax exempt properties are different.

10-33.
H_0: $\sigma_1^2 = \sigma_2^2$
H_1: $\sigma_1^2 \neq \sigma_2$ (claim)

C. V. = 2.53 $\alpha = 0.10$
d. f. N = 14   d. f. D = 14
$F = \frac{s_1^2}{s_2^2} = \frac{(1.3)^2}{(0.9)^2} = 2.09$

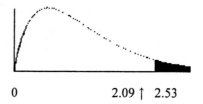

0   2.09 ↑   2.53

Do not reject the null hypothesis. There is not enough evidence to support the claim that the variations of the lengths of newborn males is different than the variations of the lengths of newborn females.

10-35.
H_0: $\sigma_1^2 \leq \sigma_2^2$

H_1: $\sigma_1^2 > \sigma_2^2$ (claim)

Chapter 10 - Testing the Difference
Between Two Means, Two Variances, and Two Proportions

10-35. continued

C. V. = 2.66 $\alpha = 0.01$

d. f. N = 27   d. f. D = 24

$F = \frac{s_1^2}{s_2^2} = \frac{(6.2)^2}{(2.7)^2} = 5.27$

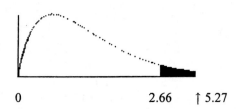

0   2.66   ↑ 5.27

Reject the null hypothesis. There is enough evidence to support the claim that the variation of blood pressure of overweight individuals is greater than the variation of blood pressure of normal weight individuals.

10-37.

$H_0: \sigma_1^2 \le \sigma_2^2$

$H_1: \sigma_1^2 > \sigma_2^2$ (claim)

C. V. = 2.90 $\alpha = 0.05$

d. f. N = 9   d. f. D = 11

$F = \frac{s_1^2}{s_2^2} = \frac{(6.3)^2}{(4.8)^2} = 1.72$

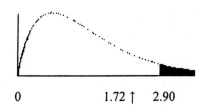

0   1.72 ↑   2.90

Do not reject the null hypothesis. There is not enough evidence to support the claim that the variation in pounds lost following Diet A is greater than the variation in pounds lost from Diet B.

10-39.

$H_0: \sigma_1^2 = \sigma_2^2$ (claim)

$H_1: \sigma_1^2 \ne \sigma_2$

$s_1 = 130.496$ $s_2 = 73.215$

C. V. = 3.87 $\alpha = 0.10$

d. f. N = 6   d. f. D = 7

$F = \frac{s_1^2}{s_2^2} = \frac{(130.496)^2}{(73.215)^2} = 3.18$

10-39. continued

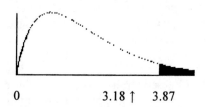

0   3.18 ↑   3.87

Do not reject the null hypothesis. There is not enough evidence to reject the claim that the variances of the heights are equal.

10-41.

Men	Women
$s_1^2 = 2.363$	$s_2^2 = 0.444$
$n_1 = 15$	$n_2 = 15$

$H_0: \sigma_1^2 = \sigma_2^2$ (claim)

$H_1: \sigma_1^2 \ne \sigma_2$

$\alpha = 0.05$ P-value = 0.004

d. f. N = 14   d. f. D = 14

$F = \frac{s_1^2}{s_2^2} = \frac{2.363}{0.444} = 5.32$

Since P-value < 0.01, reject the null hypothesis. There is enough evidence to reject the claim that the variances in weights are equal.

10-43.

$H_0: \sigma_1^2 = \sigma_2^2$

$H_1: \sigma_1^2 \ne \sigma_2^2$

d. f. N = 9   d. f. D = 9 $\alpha = 0.05$

$F = \frac{3256^2}{2341^2} = 1.93$ C. V. = 4.03

Do not reject. The variances are equal.

$H_0: \mu_1 = \mu_2$

$H_1: \mu_1 \ne \mu_2$ (claim)

C. V. = ± 2.101 d. f. = 18

$t = \frac{(\overline{X}_1 - \overline{X}_2) - (\mu_1 - \mu_2)}{\sqrt{\frac{(n_1-1)s_1^2 + (n_2-1)s_2^2}{n_1+n_2-2}}\sqrt{\frac{1}{n_1} + \frac{1}{n_2}}}$

$t = \frac{(83,256 - 88,354) - 0}{\sqrt{\frac{9(3256)^2 + 9(2341)^2}{18}}\sqrt{\frac{1}{10} + \frac{1}{10}}}$

$t = -4.02$

82

10-43. continued

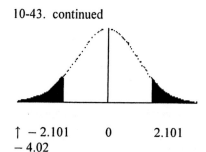

$\uparrow -2.101 \qquad 0 \qquad 2.101$
-4.02

Reject the null hypothesis. There is enough evidence to support the claim that there is a significant difference in the values of the homes based upon the appraisers' values.

Confidence Interval:

$$-5098 - 2.101 \left(\sqrt{\frac{9(3256)^2 + 9(2341)^2}{18}} \right.$$

$$\left. \sqrt{\frac{1}{10} + \frac{1}{10}} \right) < \mu_1 - \mu_2 <$$

$$-5098 + 2.101 \left(\sqrt{\frac{9(3256)^2 + 9(2341)^2}{18}} \right.$$

$$\left. \sqrt{\frac{1}{10} + \frac{1}{10}} \right) =$$

$$-5098 - 2.101(1268.14) < \mu_1 - \mu_2 <$$
$$-5098 + 2.101(1268.14)$$

$$-\$7762 < \mu_1 - \mu_2 < -\$2434$$

10-45.
H_0: $\sigma_1^2 = \sigma_2^2$
H_1: $\sigma_1^2 \neq \sigma_2^2$
d. f. N = 17   d. f. D = 11 $\alpha = 0.10$
$F = \frac{9^2}{4^2} = 5.06$ C. V. = 2.72
Reject. The variances are unequal.

H_0: $\mu_1 \geq \mu_2$
H_1: $\mu_1 < \mu_2$ (claim)

C. V. = -1.363 d. f. = 11

$$t = \frac{(\overline{X}_1 - \overline{X}_2) - (\mu_1 - \mu_2)}{\sqrt{\frac{s_1^2}{n_1} + \frac{s_2^2}{n_2}}} = \frac{(36 - 39) - 0}{\sqrt{\frac{4^2}{12} + \frac{9^2}{18}}}$$

$$t = -1.24$$

$-1.363 \quad \uparrow \quad 0$
$\qquad -1.24$

10-45. continued
Do not reject the null hypothesis. There is not enough evidence to support the claim that math majors can write and debug a program faster than business majors.

10-47.
H_0: $\sigma_1^2 = \sigma_2^2$
H_1: $\sigma_1^2 \neq \sigma_2^2$
$\overline{X}_1 = 37.167 \qquad \overline{X}_2 = 25$
$s_1 = 13.2878 \qquad s_2 = 15.7734$
d. f. N = 5   d. f. D = 5 $\alpha = 0.01$
$F = \frac{15.7734^2}{13.2878^2} = 1.41$ C. V. = 14.94
Do not reject. The variances are equal.

H_0: $\mu_1 \leq \mu_2$
H_1: $\mu_1 > \mu_2$ (claim)

C. V. = 2.764   d. f. = 10

$$t = \frac{(\overline{X}_1 - \overline{X}_2) - (\mu_1 - \mu_2)}{\sqrt{\frac{(n_1 - 1)s_1^2 + (n_2 - 1)s_2^2}{n_1 + n_2 - 2}} \sqrt{\frac{1}{n_1} + \frac{1}{n_2}}}$$

$$t = \frac{(37.167 - 25) - 0}{\sqrt{\frac{5(13.2878)^2 + 5(15.7734)^2}{6 + 6 - 2}} \sqrt{\frac{1}{6} + \frac{1}{6}}} = 1.45$$

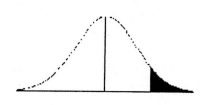

$0 \; 1.45 \uparrow 2.764$

Do not reject the null hypothesis. There is not enough evidence to support the claim that the average number of family day care centers is greater than the average number of day care centers.

10-49.
H_0: $\sigma_1^2 = \sigma_2^2$
H_1: $\sigma_1^2 \neq \sigma_2^2$
d. f. N = 9   d. f. D = 13 $\alpha = 0.02$
$F = \frac{5.6^2}{4.3^2} = 1.7$ C. V. = 4.19
Do not reject. The variances are equal.

H_0: $\mu_1 = \mu_2$
H_1: $\mu_1 \neq \mu_2$ (claim)

C. V. = ± 2.508 d. f. = 22

$$t = \frac{(\overline{X}_1 - \overline{X}_2) - (\mu_1 - \mu_2)}{\sqrt{\frac{(n_1 - 1)s_1^2 + (n_2 - 1)s_2^2}{n_1 + n_2 - 2}} \sqrt{\frac{1}{n_1} + \frac{1}{n_2}}}$$

10-49. continued

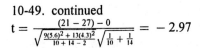

$$t = \frac{(21 - 27) - 0}{\sqrt{\frac{9(5.6)^2 + 13(4.3)^2}{10 + 14 - 2}}\sqrt{\frac{1}{10} + \frac{1}{14}}} = -2.97$$

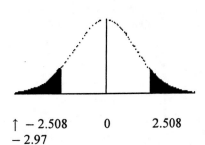

↑ -2.508 0 2.508
-2.97

Reject the null hypothesis. There is enough evidence to support the claim that there is a difference in the average times of the two groups.

Confidence Interval:
$-6 - 2.508(2.02) < \mu_1 - \mu_2 <$
$\qquad\qquad -6 + 2.508(2.02)$
$-11.1 < \mu_1 - \mu_2 < -0.93$

10-51.

$H_0: \sigma_1^2 = \sigma_2^2$
$H_1: \sigma_1^2 \neq \sigma_2^2$
d. f. N = 26   d. f. D = 11 $\alpha = 0.05$
$F = \frac{5.75^2}{3^2} = 3.67$ P-value = 0.028

$0.02 <$ P-value < 0.05 (0.028) Reject. The variances are unequal.

$H_0: \mu_1 \geq \mu_2$
$H_1: \mu_1 < \mu_2$ (claim)

P-value < 0.005 d. f. = 11

$$t = \frac{(\overline{X}_1 - \overline{X}_2) - (\mu_1 - \mu_2)}{\sqrt{\frac{s_1^2}{n_1} + \frac{s_2^2}{n_2}}} = \frac{(56 - 63) - 0}{\sqrt{\frac{3^2}{12} + \frac{5.75^2}{27}}}$$
$t = -4.98$

Since P-value < 0.05, reject the null hypothesis. There is enough evidence to support the claim that the nurses pay more for insurance than the administrators.

10-53.

White Mice	Brown Mice
$\overline{X}_1 = 17$	$\overline{X}_2 = 16.67$
$s_1 = 4.56$	$s_2 = 5.05$
$n_1 = 6$	$n_2 = 6$

10-53. continued

$H_0: \sigma_1^2 = \sigma_2^2$
$H_1: \sigma_1^2 \neq \sigma_2^2$
d. f. N = 5   d. f. D = 5 $\alpha = 0.05$

$F = \frac{5.05^2}{4.56^2} = 1.23$ C. V. = 7.15
Do not reject. The variances are equal.

$H_0: \mu_1 = \mu_2$
$H_1: \mu_1 \neq \mu_2$ (claim)

C. V. = ± 2.228 d. f. = 10

$$t = \frac{(17 - 16.67) - 0}{\sqrt{\frac{5(4.56)^2 + 5(5.05)^2}{6 + 6 - 2}}\sqrt{\frac{1}{6} + \frac{1}{6}}} = 0.119$$

-2.228 0 ↑ 2.228
          0.119

Do not reject the null hypothesis. There is not enough evidence to support the claim that the color of the mice made a difference.

Confidence Interval:
$0.33 - 2.228(2.78) < \mu_1 - \mu_2 <$
$\qquad\qquad 0.33 + 2.228(2.78)$
$-5.86 < \mu_1 - \mu_2 < 6.52$

10-55.
a. dependent
b. dependent
c. independent
d. dependent
e. independent

10-57.

Before	After	D	D²
9	9	0	0
12	17	-5	25
6	9	-3	9
15	20	-5	25
3	2	1	1
18	21	-3	9
10	15	-5	25
13	22	-9	81
7	6	1	1
		$\sum D = -28$	$\sum D^2 = 176$

10-57. continued

H_0: $\mu_D \geq 0$

H_1: $\mu_D < 0$ (claim)

C. V. = -1.397 d. f. = 8

$\overline{D} = \frac{\sum D}{n} = -3.11$

$s_D = \sqrt{\frac{\sum D^2 - \frac{(\sum D)^2}{n}}{n-1}} = \sqrt{\frac{176 - \frac{(-28)^2}{9}}{8}} = 3.33$

$t = \frac{-3.11 - 0}{\frac{3.33}{\sqrt{9}}} = -2.8$

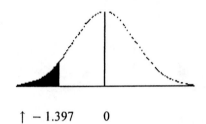

↑ -1.397 0
-2.8

Reject the null hypothesis. There is enough evidence to support the claim that the seminar increased the number of hours students studied.

10-59.

Before	After	D	D ^{2}
146	135	11	121
138	133	5	25
152	147	5	25
163	156	7	49
136	138	-2	4
147	141	6	36
148	139	9	81
141	132	9	81
143	138	5	25
142	131	11	121
		$\sum D = 66$	$\sum D^2 = 568$

H_0: $\mu_D \leq 0$

H_1: $\mu_D > 0$ (claim)

C. V. = 1.833   d. f. = 9

$\overline{D} = \frac{\sum D}{n} = \frac{66}{10} = 6.6$

$s_D = \sqrt{\frac{\sum D^2 - \frac{(\sum D)^2}{n}}{n-1}} = \sqrt{\frac{568 - \frac{(66)^2}{10}}{9}} = 5.77$

$t = \frac{6.6 - 0}{\frac{3.84}{\sqrt{10}}} = 5.435$

10-59. continued

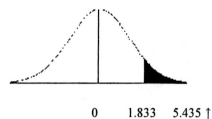

0   1.833   5.435 ↑

Reject the null hypothesis. There is enough evidence to support the claim that the diet reduced the sodium level of the patients.

10-61.

Before	After	D	D ^{2}
12	9	3	9
9	6	3	9
0	1	-1	1
5	3	2	4
4	2	2	4
3	3	0	0
		$\sum D = 9$	$\sum D^2 = 27$

H_0: $\mu_D \leq 0$

H_1: $\mu_D > 0$ (claim)

C. V. = 2.571   d. f. = 5

$\overline{D} = \frac{\sum D}{n} = \frac{9}{6} = 1.5$

$s_D = \sqrt{\frac{\sum D^2 - \frac{(\sum D)^2}{n}}{n-1}} = \sqrt{\frac{27 - \frac{9^2}{6}}{5}} = 1.64$

$t = \frac{1.5 - 0}{\frac{1.64}{\sqrt{6}}} = 2.24$

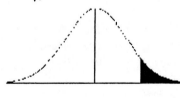

0   ↑ 2.571
       2.24

Do not reject the null hypothesis. There is not enough evidence to support the claim that the errors have been reduced.

10-63.

A	B	D	D^2
87	83	4	16
92	95	-3	9
78	79	-1	1
83	83	0	0
88	86	2	4
90	93	-3	9
84	80	4	16
93	86	7	49

$$\sum D = 10 \quad \sum D^2 = 104$$

$H_0: \mu_D = 0$
$H_1: \mu_D \neq 0$ (claim)

P-value = 0.361   d. f. = 7

$$\overline{D} = \frac{\sum D}{n} = \frac{10}{8} = 1.25$$

$$s_D = \sqrt{\frac{\sum D^2 - \frac{(\sum D)^2}{n}}{n-1}} = \sqrt{\frac{104 - \frac{10^2}{8}}{7}} = 3.62$$

$$t = \frac{1.25 - 0}{\frac{3.62}{\sqrt{8}}} = 0.977$$

0.20 < P-value < 0.50 Do not reject the null hypothesis since P-value > 0.01. There is not enough evidence to support the claim that there is a difference in the pulse rates.

Confidence Interval:
$$1.25 - 3.499\left(\frac{3.62}{\sqrt{8}}\right) < \mu_D <$$
$$1.25 + 3.499\left(\frac{3.62}{\sqrt{8}}\right)$$
$$-3.23 < \mu_D < 5.73$$

10-65.
Using the previous problem, $\overline{D} = -1.5625$ whereas the mean of the 1994 values is 95.375 and the mean of the 1999 values is 96.9375; hence,
$$\overline{D} = 95.375 - 96.9375 = -1.5625$$

10-67.
a. $x = 0.16(100) = 16$
b. $x = 0.08(50) = 4$
c. $x = 0.06(80) = 4.8$
d. $x = 0.52(200) = 104$
e. $x = 0.20(150) = 30$

10-69.
$$\hat{p}_1 = \frac{X_1}{n_1} = \frac{80}{150} = 0.533 \quad \hat{p}_2 = \frac{30}{100} = 0.3$$

10-69. continued
$$\overline{p} = \frac{X_1 + X_2}{n_1 + n_2} = \frac{80 + 30}{150 + 100} = \frac{110}{250} = 0.44$$

$$\overline{q} = 1 - \overline{p} = 1 - 0.44 = 0.56$$

$H_0: p_1 = p_2$
$H_1: p_1 \neq p_2$ (claim)

C. V. = ± 1.96

$$z = \frac{(\hat{p}_1 - \hat{p}_2) - (p_1 - p_2)}{\sqrt{(\overline{p})(\overline{q})\left(\frac{1}{n_1} + \frac{1}{n_2}\right)}} = \frac{(0.533 - 0.3) - 0}{\sqrt{(0.44)(0.56)\left(\frac{1}{150} + \frac{1}{100}\right)}}$$

$z = 3.64$

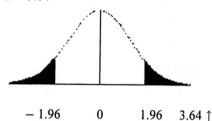

$$-1.96 \qquad 0 \qquad 1.96 \quad 3.64 \uparrow$$

Reject the null hypothesis. There is enough evidence to support the claim that there is a significant difference in the proportions.

10-71.
$$\hat{p}_1 = \frac{X_1}{n_1} = \frac{43}{100} = 0.43 \quad \hat{p}_2 = \frac{58}{100} = 0.58$$

$$\overline{p} = \frac{X_1 + X_2}{n_1 + n_2} = \frac{43 + 58}{100 + 100} = 0.505$$

$$\overline{q} = 1 - \overline{p} = 1 - 0.505 = 0.495$$

$H_0: p_1 = p_2$
$H_1: p_1 \neq p_2$ (claim)

C. V. = ± 1.96

$$z = \frac{(\hat{p}_1 - \hat{p}_2) - (p_1 - p_2)}{\sqrt{(\overline{p})(\overline{q})\left(\frac{1}{n_1} + \frac{1}{n_2}\right)}} = \frac{(0.43 - 0.58) - 0}{\sqrt{(0.505)(0.495)\left(\frac{1}{100} + \frac{1}{100}\right)}}$$

$z = -2.12$

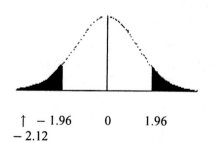

$$\uparrow -1.96 \qquad 0 \qquad 1.96$$
$$-2.12$$

10-71. continued
Reject the null hypothesis. There is enough evidence to support the claim that the proportions are different.

10-73.
$\hat{p}_1 = 0.83 \qquad \hat{p}_2 = 0.75$
$X_1 = 0.83(100) = 83$
$X_2 = 0.75(100) = 75$

$\bar{p} = \frac{83 + 75}{100 + 100} = 0.79 \quad \bar{q} = 1 - 0.79 = 0.21$

H_0: $p_1 = p_2$ (claim)
H_1: $p_1 \neq p_2$
C. V. $= \pm 1.96 \quad \alpha = 0.05$

$z = \frac{(\hat{p}_1 - \hat{p}_2) - (p_1 - p_2)}{\sqrt{(\bar{p})(\bar{q})(\frac{1}{n_1} + \frac{1}{n_2})}} = \frac{(0.83 - 0.75) - 0}{\sqrt{(0.79)(0.21)(\frac{1}{100} + \frac{1}{100})}}$

$z = 1.39$

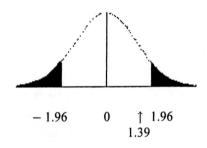

$- 1.96 \qquad 0 \qquad \uparrow 1.96$
1.39

Do not reject the null hypothesis. There is not enough evidence to reject the claim that the proportions are equal.

$(\hat{p}_1 - \hat{p}_2) - z_{\frac{\alpha}{2}} \sqrt{\frac{\hat{p}_1 \hat{q}_1}{n_1} + \frac{\hat{p}_2 \hat{q}_2}{n_2}} < p_1 - p_2 <$

$(\hat{p}_1 - \hat{p}_2) + z_{\frac{\alpha}{2}} \sqrt{\frac{\hat{p}_1 \hat{q}_1}{n_1} + \frac{\hat{p}_2 \hat{q}_2}{n_2}}$

$0.08 - 1.96 \sqrt{\frac{0.83(0.17)}{100} + \frac{0.75(0.25)}{100}} < p_1 - p_2$

$< 0.08 + 1.96 \sqrt{\frac{0.83(0.17)}{100} + \frac{0.75(0.25)}{100}}$

$- 0.032 < p_1 - p_2 < 0.192$

10-75.
$\hat{p}_1 = 0.55 \qquad \hat{p}_2 = 0.45$

$X_1 = 0.55(80) = 44 \quad X_2 = 0.45(90) = 40.5$

$\bar{p} = \frac{X_1 + X_2}{n_1 + n_2} = \frac{44 + 40.5}{80 + 90} = 0.497$

10-75. continued
$\bar{q} = 1 - \bar{p} = 1 - 0.497 = 0.503$

H_0: $p_1 = p_2$
H_1: $p_1 \neq p_2$ (claim)

C. V. $= \pm 2.58 \quad \alpha = 0.01$

$z = \frac{(\hat{p}_1 - \hat{p}_2) - (p_1 - p_2)}{\sqrt{(\bar{p})(\bar{q})(\frac{1}{n_1} + \frac{1}{n_2})}} = \frac{(0.55 - 0.45) - 0}{\sqrt{(0.497)(0.503)(\frac{1}{80} + \frac{1}{90})}}$

$z = 1.302$

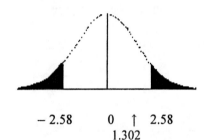

$- 2.58 \qquad 0 \uparrow 2.58$
1.302

Do not reject the null hypothesis. There is not enough evidence to support the claim that the proportions are different.

$(\hat{p}_1 - \hat{p}_2) - z_{\frac{\alpha}{2}} \sqrt{\frac{\hat{p}_1 \hat{q}_1}{n_1} + \frac{\hat{p}_2 \hat{q}_2}{n_2}} < p_1 - p_2 <$

$(\hat{p}_1 - \hat{p}_2) + z_{\frac{\alpha}{2}} \sqrt{\frac{\hat{p}_1 \hat{q}_1}{n_1} + \frac{\hat{p}_2 \hat{q}_2}{n_2}}$

$0.1 - 2.58 \sqrt{\frac{0.55(0.45)}{80} + \frac{0.45(0.55)}{90}} < p_1 - p_2$

$< 0.1 + 2.58 \sqrt{\frac{0.55(0.45)}{80} + \frac{0.45(0.55)}{90}}$

$- 0.097 < p_1 - p_2 < 0.297$

10-77.
$\hat{p}_1 = \frac{45}{80} = 0.5625 \qquad \hat{p}_2 = \frac{63}{120} = 0.525$

$\bar{p} = \frac{X_1 + X_2}{n_1 + n_2} = \frac{45 + 63}{80 + 120} = 0.54$

$\bar{q} = 1 - \bar{p} = 1 - 0.54 = 0.46$

H_0: $p_1 = p_2$
H_1: $p_1 \neq p_2$ (claim)

C. V. $= \pm 1.96 \quad \alpha = 0.05$
$z = \frac{(\hat{p}_1 - \hat{p}_2) - (p_1 - p_2)}{\sqrt{(\bar{p})(\bar{q})(\frac{1}{n_1} + \frac{1}{n_2})}} = \frac{(0.5625 - 0.525) - 0}{\sqrt{(0.54)(0.46)(\frac{1}{80} + \frac{1}{120})}}$

$z = 0.521$

10-77. continued

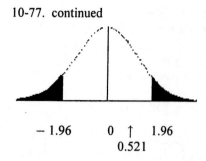

$$-1.96 \qquad 0 \uparrow \quad 1.96$$
$$0.521$$

Do not reject the null hypothesis. There is not enough evidence to support the claim that there is a difference in the proportions.

$$(\hat{p}_1 - \hat{p}_2) - z_{\frac{\alpha}{2}} \sqrt{\frac{\hat{p}_1 \hat{q}_1}{n_1} + \frac{\hat{p}_2 \hat{q}_2}{n_2}} < p_1 - p_2 <$$

$$(\hat{p}_1 - \hat{p}_2) + z_{\frac{\alpha}{2}} \sqrt{\frac{\hat{p}_1 \hat{q}_1}{n_1} + \frac{\hat{p}_2 \hat{q}_2}{n_2}}$$

$$0.0375 - 1.96 \sqrt{\frac{0.5625(0.4375)}{80} + \frac{0.525(0.475)}{120}} <$$

$$p_1 - p_2 < 0.0375 + 1.96 \sqrt{\frac{0.5625(0.4375)}{80} + \frac{0.525(0.475)}{120}}$$

$$-0.103 < p_1 - p_2 < 0.178$$

10-79.
$$\hat{p}_1 = \frac{X_1}{n_1} = \frac{50}{200} = 0.25$$

$$\hat{p}_2 = \frac{X_2}{n_2} = \frac{93}{300} = 0.31$$

$$\bar{p} = \frac{X_1 + X_2}{n_1 + n_2} = \frac{50 + 93}{200 + 300} = 0.286$$

$$\bar{q} = 1 - \bar{p} = 1 - 0.286 = 0.714$$

H_0: $p_1 = p_2$
H_1: $p_1 \neq p_2$ (claim)

C. V. $= \pm 2.58$ $\alpha = 0.01$

$$z = \frac{(\hat{p}_1 - \hat{p}_2) - (p_1 - p_2)}{\sqrt{(\bar{p})(\bar{q})(\frac{1}{n_1} + \frac{1}{n_2})}} = \frac{(0.25 - 0.31) - 0}{\sqrt{(0.286)(0.714)(\frac{1}{200} + \frac{1}{300})}}$$

$$z = -1.45$$

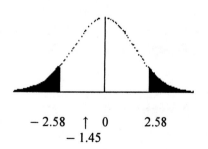

$$-2.58 \quad \uparrow \quad 0 \qquad 2.58$$
$$-1.45$$

10-79. continued
Do not reject the null hypothesis. There is not enough evidence to support the claim that the proportions are different.

$$(\hat{p}_1 - \hat{p}_2) - z_{\frac{\alpha}{2}} \sqrt{\frac{\hat{p}_1 \hat{q}_1}{n_1} + \frac{\hat{p}_2 \hat{q}_2}{n_2}} < p_1 - p_2 <$$

$$(\hat{p}_1 - \hat{p}_2) + z_{\frac{\alpha}{2}} \sqrt{\frac{\hat{p}_1 \hat{q}_1}{n_1} + \frac{\hat{p}_2 \hat{q}_2}{n_2}}$$

$$-0.06 - 2.58 \sqrt{\frac{0.25(0.75)}{200} + \frac{0.31(0.69)}{300}} <$$

$$p_1 - p_2 < -0.06 + 2.58 \sqrt{\frac{0.25(0.75)}{200} + \frac{0.31(0.69)}{300}}$$

$$-0.165 < p_1 - p_2 < 0.045$$

10-81.
$\alpha = 0.01$
$\hat{p}_1 = 0.8$ $\qquad\qquad \hat{q}_1 = 0.2$
$\hat{p}_2 = 0.6$ $\qquad\qquad \hat{q}_2 = 0.4$

$$\hat{p}_1 - \hat{p}_2 = 0.8 - 0.6 = 0.2$$

$$(\hat{p}_1 - \hat{p}_2) - z_{\frac{\alpha}{2}} \sqrt{\frac{\hat{p}_1 \hat{q}_1}{n_1} + \frac{\hat{p}_2 \hat{q}_2}{n_2}} < p_1 - p_2 <$$

$$(\hat{p}_1 - \hat{p}_2) + z_{\frac{\alpha}{2}} \sqrt{\frac{\hat{p}_1 \hat{q}_1}{n_1} + \frac{\hat{p}_2 \hat{q}_2}{n_2}}$$

$$0.2 - 2.58 \sqrt{\frac{(0.8)(0.2)}{150} + \frac{(0.6)(0.4)}{200}} < p_1 - p_2 <$$

$$0.2 + 2.58 \sqrt{\frac{(0.8)(0.2)}{150} + \frac{(0.6)(0.4)}{200}}$$

$$0.077 < p_1 - p_2 < 0.323$$

10-83.
No, because p_1 could equal p_2.

10-85.
H_0: $\mu_1 \leq \mu_2$
H_1: $\mu_1 > \mu_2$ (claim)

CV $= 2.33$ $\qquad \alpha = 0.01$
$\bar{X}_1 = 120.1$ $\qquad \bar{X}_2 = 117.8$
$s_1 = 16.722$ $\qquad s_2 = 16.053$

$$z = \frac{(\bar{X}_1 - \bar{X}_2) - (\mu_1 - \mu_2)}{\sqrt{\frac{s_1^2}{n_1} + \frac{s_2^2}{n_2}}} = \frac{(120.1 - 117.8) - 0}{\sqrt{\frac{16.722^2}{36} + \frac{16.053^2}{35}}}$$

$$z = 0.587$$

10-85. continued

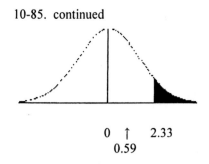

$$0 \quad \uparrow \quad 2.33$$
$$0.59$$

Do not reject the null hypothesis. There is not enough evidence to support the claim that single people do more pleasure driving than married people.

10-87.
$H_0: \sigma_1 = \sigma_2$
$H_1: \sigma_1 \neq \sigma_2$ (claim)

C. V. = 2.77 $\alpha = 0.10$
d. f. N = 23   d. f. D = 10

$F = \frac{13.2^2}{4.1^2} = 10.365$

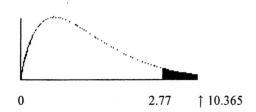

$$0 \qquad\qquad 2.77 \qquad \uparrow 10.365$$

Reject the null hypothesis. There is enough evidence to support the claim that there is a difference in standard deviations.

10-89.
$H_0: \sigma_1^2 \leq \sigma_2^2$
$H_1: \sigma_1^2 > \sigma_2^2$ (claim)

$\alpha = 0.05$
d. f. N = 9   d. f. D = 9
$F = \frac{s_1^2}{s_2^2} = \frac{6.3^2}{2.8^2} = 5.06$

The P-value for the F test is $0.01 <$ P-value < 0.025 (0.012). Since P-value < 0.05, reject the null hypothesis. There is enough evidence to support the claim that the variance of the number of speeding tickets on Route 19 is greater than the variance of the number of speeding tickets issued on Route 22.

10-91.
$H_0: \sigma_1^2 \leq \sigma_2^2$
$H_1: \sigma_1^2 > \sigma_2^2$ (claim)

C. V. = 1.47 $\alpha = 0.10$
d. f. N = 64   d. f. D = 41

$F = \frac{s_1^2}{s_2^2} = \frac{3.2^2}{2.1^2} = 2.32$

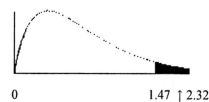

$$0 \qquad\qquad\qquad 1.47 \uparrow 2.32$$

Reject the null hypothesis. There is enough evidence to support the claim that the variation in the number of days factory workers miss per year due to illness is greater than the variation in the number of days hospital workers miss per year.

10-93.
$\overline{X}_1 = 72.9$ $\overline{X}_2 = 70.8$
$s_1 = 5.5$ $s_2 = 5.8$

$H_0: \sigma_1^2 = \sigma_2^2$

CV = 1.98 $\alpha = 0.01$
$F = \frac{5.8^2}{5.5^2} = 1.11$
Do not reject H_0. The variances are equal.

$H_0: \mu_1 \leq \mu_2$
$H_1: \mu_1 > \mu_2$ (claim)

C. V. = 1.28   d. f. = 48 $\alpha = 0.10$

$$t = \frac{(\overline{X}_1 - \overline{X}_2) - (\mu_1 - \mu_2)}{\sqrt{\frac{(n_1 - 1)s_1^2 + (n_2 - 1)s_2^2}{n_1 + n_2 - 2}}\sqrt{\frac{1}{n_1} + \frac{1}{n_2}}}$$

$$t = \frac{(72.9 - 70.8) - 0}{\sqrt{\frac{24(5.5)^2 + 24(5.8)^2}{25 + 25 - 2}}\sqrt{\frac{1}{25} + \frac{1}{25}}} = 1.31$$

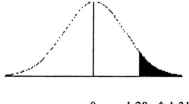

$$0 \qquad 1.28 \uparrow 1.31$$

10-93. continued

Reject the null hypothesis. There is enough evidence to support the claim that it is warmer in Birmingham.

10-95.

$H_0: \sigma_1^2 = \sigma_2^2$

$\alpha = 0.05$

$F = \frac{8256^2}{1311^2} = 39.66$

Reject since P-value < 0.05. The variances are unequal.

$H_0: \mu_1 \leq \mu_2$
$H_1: \mu_1 > \mu_2$ (claim)

$\alpha = 0.05$ d. f. $= 11$

$t = \frac{(54,356 - 46,512) - 0}{\sqrt{\frac{8256^2}{16} + \frac{1311^2}{12}}} = 3.74$

P-value < 0.005

Reject the null hypothesis since P-value < 0.05. There is enough evidence to support the claim that incomes of the city residents are greater than the incomes of the suburban residents.

10-97.

Before	After	D	D²
6	10	-4	16
8	12	-4	16
10	9	1	1
9	12	-3	9
5	8	-3	9
12	13	-1	1
9	8	1	1
7	10	-3	9

$\sum D = -16$ $\sum D^2 = 62$

$H_0: \mu_D \geq 0$
$H_1: \mu_D < 0$ (claim)

C. V. $= -1.895$ d. f. $= 7$ $\alpha = 0.05$

$\overline{D} = \frac{\sum D}{n} = \frac{-16}{8} = -2$

$s_D = \sqrt{\frac{62 - \frac{(-16)^2}{8}}{7}} = 2.07$

$t = \frac{-2 - 0}{\frac{2.07}{\sqrt{8}}} = -2.73$

10-97. continued

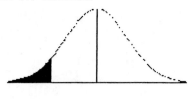

↑ -1.895 0
-2.73

Reject the null hypothesis. There is enough evidence to support the claim that the music has increased production.

10-99.

$\hat{p}_1 = \frac{32}{50} = 0.64$ $\hat{p}_2 = \frac{24}{60} = 0.40$

$\overline{p} = \frac{32 + 24}{50 + 60} = 0.509$

$\overline{q} = 1 - 0.509 = 0.491$

$H_0: p_1 = p_2$ (claim)
$H_1: p_1 \neq p_2$

C. V. $= \pm 1.96$ $\alpha = 0.05$

$z = \frac{(0.64 - 0.40) - 0}{\sqrt{(0.509)(0.491)(\frac{1}{50} + \frac{1}{60})}} = 2.51$

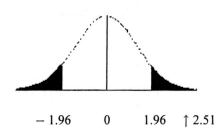

-1.96 0 1.96 ↑ 2.51

Reject the null hypothesis. There is enough evidence to reject the claim that the proportions are equal.

For the 95% confidence interval:

$\hat{p}_1 = 0.64$ $\hat{q}_1 = 0.36$
$\hat{p}_2 = 0.4$ $\hat{q}_2 = 0.6$

$(0.64 - 0.4) - 1.96\sqrt{\frac{(0.64)(0.36)}{50} + \frac{(0.4)(0.6)}{60}}$

$< p_1 - p_2 < (0.64 - 0.4) + 1.96\sqrt{\frac{(0.64)(0.36)}{50} + \frac{(0.4)(0.6)}{60}}$

$0.24 - 1.96(0.0928) < p_1 - p_2 <$

$0.24 + 1.96(0.0928)$

10-99. continued
$0.058 < p_1 - p_2 < 0.422$

Quiz:
1. False, there are different formulas for independent and dependent samples.
2. False, the samples are independent.
3. True
4. False, they can be right, left, or two tailed.
5. d
6. a
7. c
8. b
9. $\mu_1 = \mu_2$
10. pooled
11. normal
12. negative
13. $\frac{s_1^2}{s_2^2}$

14. H_0: $\mu_1 = \mu_2$
H_1: $\mu_1 \neq \mu_2$ (claim)
C. V. $= \pm 2.58$ $z = -3.69$
Reject the null hypothesis. There is enough evidence to support the claim that there is a difference in the cholesterol levels of the two groups.
99% Confidence Interval:
$-10.2 < \mu_1 - \mu_2 < -1.8$

15. H_0: $\mu_1 \leq \mu_2$
H_1: $\mu_1 > \mu_2$ (claim)
C. V. $= 1.28$ $z = 1.60$
Reject the null hypothesis. There is enough evidence to support the claim that average rental fees for the east apartments is greater than the average rental fees for the west apartments.

16. H_0: $\sigma_1^2 = \sigma_2^2$
H_1: $\sigma_1^2 \neq \sigma_1^2$ (claim)
F $= 1.637$ P-value > 0.20 (0.357)
Do not reject the null hypothesis since P-value > 0.05. There is not enough evidence to support the claim that the variances are different.

17. H_0: $\sigma_1^2 = \sigma_2^2$
H_1: $\sigma_1^2 \neq \sigma_2^2$ (claim)
C. V. $= 1.90$ F $= 2.90$
Reject the null hypothesis. There is enough evidence to support the claim that the variances are different.

18. H_0: $\sigma_1^2 = \sigma_2^2$ (claim)
H_1 $\sigma_1^2 \neq \sigma_2^2$
C. V. $= 3.53$ F $= 1.13$
Do not reject the null hypothesis. There is not enough evidence to reject the claim that the standard deviations or the number of hours of television viewing are the same.

19. H_0: $\sigma_1^2 = \sigma_2^2$
H_1 $\sigma_1^2 \neq \sigma_2^2$ (claim)
C. V. $= 3.01$ F $= 1.94$
Do not reject the null hypothesis. There is enough evidence to support the claim that the variances are different.

20. H_0: $\sigma_1^2 \leq \sigma_2^2$
H_1 $\sigma_1^2 > \sigma_2^2$ (claim)
C. V. $= 1.44$ F $= 1.474$
Reject the null hypothesis. There is enough evidence to support the claim that the variance of days missed by teachers is greater than the variance of days missed by nurses.

21. H_0: $\sigma_1 = \sigma_2$
H_1 $\sigma_1 \neq \sigma_2$ (claim)
C. V. $= 2.46$ F $= 1.65$
Do not reject the null hypothesis. There is not enough evidence to support the claim that the standard deviations are different.

22. H_0: $\sigma_1^2 = \sigma_2^2$

C. V. $= 5.05$ F $= 1.23$
Do not reject. The variances are equal.

H_0: $\mu_1 = \mu_2$
H_1: $\mu_1 \neq \mu_2$ (claim)
C. V. $= \pm 2.779$ $t = 10.92$

Reject the null hypothesis. There is enough evidence to support the claim that the average prices are different.

99% Confidence Interval:
$0.298 < \mu_1 - \mu_2 < 0.502$

23. H_0: $\sigma_1^2 = \sigma_2^2$
H_1 $\sigma_1^2 \neq \sigma_2^2$
C. V. $= 9.6$ F $= 5.71$
Reject. The variances are not equal.

H_0: $\mu_1 \geq \mu_2$
H_1: $\mu_1 < \mu_2$ (claim)

23. continued

C. V. $= -1.860$ $\qquad$ t $= -4.05$

Reject the null hypothesis. There is not enough evidence to support the claim that accidents have increased.

24. H_0: $\sigma_1^2 = \sigma_2^2$

C. V. $= 4.02$ $\qquad$ F $= 6.155$

Reject. The variances are unequal.

H_0: $\mu_1 = \mu_2$
H_1: $\mu_1 \neq \mu_2$ (claim)
C. V. $= \pm 2.718$ $\qquad$ t $= 9.807$
Reject the null hypothesis. There is enough evidence to support the claim that the salaries are different.

98% Confidence Interval:
$\$6652 < \mu_1 - \mu_2 < \$11,757$

25. H_0: $\sigma_1^2 = \sigma_2^2$

F $= 23.08$ $\qquad$ P-value < 0.05
Reject. The variances are unequal.

H_0: $\mu_1 \leq \mu_2$
H_1: $\mu_1 > \mu_2$ (claim)

t $= 0.874$ $\qquad$ d. f. = 10
$0.10 < $ P-value < 0.25 (0.198)

Do not reject the null hypothesis since P-value > 0.05. There is not enough evidence to support the claim that incomes of city residents is greater than incomes of rural residents.

26. H_0: $\mu_1 \geq \mu_2$
H_1: $\mu_1 < \mu_2$ (claim)
$\overline{D} = -6.5$ $\qquad$ $s_D = 4.93$
C. V. $= -2.821$ $\qquad$ t $= -4.17$
Reject the null hypothesis. There is enough evidence to support the claim that the sessions improved math skills.

27. H_0: $\mu_1 \geq \mu_2$
H_1: $\mu_1 < \mu_2$ (claim)
$\overline{D} = -0.8$ $\qquad$ $s_D = 1.48$
C. V. $= -1.833$ $\qquad$ t $= -1.71$
Do not reject the null hypothesis. There is not enough evidence to support the claim that egg production increased.

28. H_0: $p_1 = p_2$
H_1: $p_1 \neq p_2$ (claim)
C. V. $= \pm 1.65$ $\quad$ z $= -0.69$
Do not reject the null hypothesis. There is not enough evidence to support the claim that the proportions are different.

90% Confidence Interval:
$-0.101 < p_1 - p_2 < 0.041$

29. H_0: $p_1 = p_2$ (claim)
H_1: $p_1 \neq p_2$
C. V. $= \pm 1.96$ $\quad$ z $= 2.58$
Reject the null hypothesis. There is enough evidence to reject the claim that the proportions are equal.

95% Confidence Interval:
$0.067 < p_1 - p_2 < 0.445$

Note: Graphs are not to scale and are intended to convey a general idea. Answers may vary due to rounding.

11-1.
Two variables are related when there exists a discernible pattern between them.

11-3.
r, ρ

11-5.
A positive relationship means that as x increases, y also increases.
A negative relationship means that as x increases, y decreases.

11-7.
Answers will vary.

11-9.
Pearson's Product Moment Correlation Coefficient.

11-11.
There are many other possibilities, such as chance, relationship to a third variable, etc.

11-13.

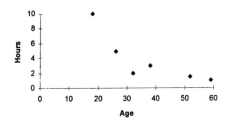

$\sum x = 225$
$\sum y = 22.5$
$\sum x^2 = 9653$
$\sum y^2 = 141.25$
$\sum xy = 625$
$n = 6$

$$r = \frac{n(\sum xy)-(\sum x)(\sum y)}{\sqrt{[n(\sum x^2)-(\sum x)^2][n(\sum y^2)-(\sum y)^2]}}$$

$$r = \frac{6(625)-(225)(22.5)}{\sqrt{[6(9653)-(225)^2][6(141.25)-(22.5)^2]}}$$

$r = -0.832$

H_0: $\rho = 0$ and H_1: $\rho \neq 0$; C. V. = ± 0.811; d. f. = 4; Decision: reject; there is a significant relationship between a person's

11-13. continued
age and the number of hours a person watches television.

11-15.

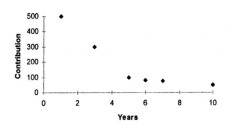

$\sum x = 32$
$\sum y = 1105$
$\sum x^2 = 220$
$\sum y^2 = 364,525$
$\sum xy = 3405$
$n = 6$

$$r = \frac{n(\sum xy)-(\sum x)(\sum y)}{\sqrt{[n(\sum x^2)-(\sum x)^2][n(\sum y^2)-(\sum y)^2]}}$$

$$r = \frac{6(3405)-(32)(1105)}{\sqrt{[6(220)-(32)^2][6(364525)-(1105)^2]}}$$

$r = -0.883$

H_0: $\rho = 0$
H_1: $\rho \neq 0$
C. V. = ± 0.811 d. f. = 4

Decision: Reject. There is a significant relationship between a person's age and his or her contribution.

11-17.

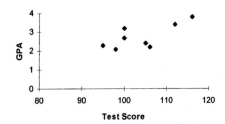

$\sum x = 832$
$\sum y = 22.1$
$\sum x^2 = 86,890$
$\sum y^2 = 63.83$
$\sum xy = 2321.1$
$n = 8$

$$r = \frac{n(\sum xy)-(\sum x)(\sum y)}{\sqrt{[n(\sum x^2)-(\sum x)^2][n(\sum y^2)-(\sum y)^2]}}$$

$$r = \frac{8(2321.1)-(832)(22.1)}{\sqrt{[8(86,890)-(832)^2][8(63.83)-(22.1)^2]}}$$

11-17. continued
r = 0.716

H_0: $\rho = 0$
H_1: $\rho \neq 0$
C. V. = ± 0.707   d. f. = 6

Decision: Reject. There is a significant relationship between test scores and G. P. A.

11-19.

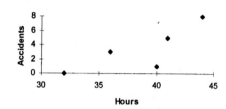

$\sum x = 193$
$\sum y = 17$
$\sum x^2 = 7537$
$\sum y^2 = 99$
$\sum xy = 705$
n = 5

$$r = \frac{n(\sum xy)-(\sum x)(\sum y)}{\sqrt{[n(\sum x^2)-(\sum x)^2]\,[n(\sum y^2)-(\sum y)^2]}}$$

r = 0.814

H_0: $\rho = 0$
H_1: $\rho \neq 0$
C. V. = ± 0.878   d. f. = 3

Decision: Do not reject. There is not a significant relationship between the variables.

11-21.

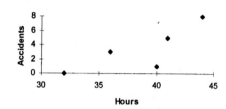

$\sum x = 2223$
$\sum y = 5859$
$\sum x^2 = 766,671$
$\sum y^2 = 5,386,165$
$\sum xy = 1,836,199$
n = 7

11-21. continued

$$r = \frac{n(\sum xy)-(\sum x)(\sum y)}{\sqrt{[n(\sum x^2)-(\sum x)^2]\,[n(\sum y^2)-(\sum y)^2]}}$$

$$r = \frac{7(1,836,199) - (2223)(5859)}{\sqrt{[7(766,761) - 2223^2][7(5,386,165) - 5859^2]}}$$

r = − 0.143

H_0: $\rho = 0$
H_1: $\rho \neq 0$
C. V. = ± 0.754   d. f. = 5

Decision: Do not reject. There is no significant relationship between calories and sodium content.

11-23.

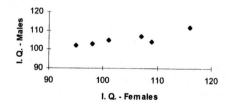

$\sum x = 67.5$
$\sum y = 2610$
$\sum x^2 = 653.11$
$\sum y^2 = 981,500$
$\sum xy = 25,292$
n = 7

$$r = \frac{n(\sum xy)-(\sum x)(\sum y)}{\sqrt{[n(\sum x^2)-(\sum x)^2]\,[n(\sum y^2)-(\sum y)^2]}}$$

$$r = \frac{7(25,292) - (67.5)(2610)}{\sqrt{[7(653.11) - 67.5^2][7(981,500) - 2610^2]}}$$

r = 0.913

H_0: $\rho = 0$
H_1: $\rho \neq 0$
C. V. = ± 0.754   d. f. = 5

Decision: Reject. There is a significant relationship between energy efficiency ratings and cost.

11-25.

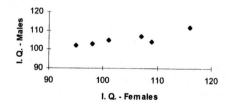

11-25. continued

$\sum x = 626$
$\sum y = 633$
$\sum x^2 = 65616$
$\sum y^2 = 66847$
$\sum xy = 66166$
$n = 6$

$r = \dfrac{n(\sum xy)-(\sum x)(\sum y)}{\sqrt{[n(\sum x^2)-(\sum x)^2]\,[n(\sum y^2)-(\sum y)^2]}}$

$r = \dfrac{6(66166)-(626)(633)}{\sqrt{[6(65616)-(626)^2][6(66847)-(633)^2]}}$

$r = \dfrac{396996-396258}{\sqrt{(1820)(393)}} = \dfrac{738}{845.73045} = 0.873$

H_0: $\rho = 0$
H_1: $\rho \neq 0$
C. V. = ± 0.811 d. f. = 4

Decision: Reject There is a significant relationship between the I. Q.'s of the girls and the boys.

11-27.

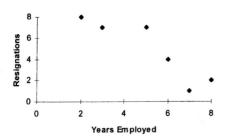

$\sum x = 31$
$\sum y = 29$
$\sum x^2 = 187$
$\sum y^2 = 183$
$\sum xy = 119$
$n = 6$

$r = \dfrac{n(\sum xy)-(\sum x)(\sum y)}{\sqrt{[n(\sum x^2)-(\sum x)^2]\,[n(\sum y^2)-(\sum y)^2]}}$

$r = -0.909$

H_0: $\rho = 0$
H_1: $\rho \neq 0$
C. V. = ± 0.811 d. f. = 4

Decision: Reject.
There is a significant relationship between the years of service and the number of resignations.

11-29.

$r = \dfrac{n(\sum xy)-(\sum x)(\sum y)}{\sqrt{[n(\sum x^2)-(\sum x)^2]\,[n(\sum y^2)-(\sum y)^2]}}$

11-29. continued

$r = \dfrac{5(125)-(15)(35)}{\sqrt{[5(55)-(15)^2][5(285)-(35)^2]}} = 1$

$r = \dfrac{5(125)-(35)(15)}{\sqrt{[5(285)-(35)^2][5(55)-(15)^2]}} = 1$

The value of r does not change when the values for x and y are interchanged.

11-31.
Draw the scatter plot and test the significance of the correlation coefficient.

11-33.
$y' = a + bx$

11-35.
It is the line that is drawn through the points on the scatter plot such that the sum of the squares of the vertical distances each point is from the line is a minimum.

11-37.
When r is positive, b will be positive. When r is negative, b will be negative.

11-39.
The closer r is to +1 or -1, the more accurate the predicted value will be.

11-41.
$a = \dfrac{(\sum y)(\sum x^2)-(\sum x)(\sum xy)}{n(\sum x^2)-(\sum x)^2}$

$a = \dfrac{(22.5)(9653)-(225)(625)}{6(9653)-(225)^2} = 10.499$

$b = \dfrac{n(\sum xy)-(\sum x)(\sum y)}{n(\sum x^2)-(\sum x)^2}$

$b = \dfrac{6(625)-(225)(22.5)}{6(9653)-(225)^2} = -0.18$

$y' = a + bx$
$y' = 10.499 + -0.18x$
$y' = 10.499 + -0.18(35) = 4.199$ hours

11-43.
$a = \dfrac{(\sum y)(\sum x^2)-(\sum x)(\sum xy)}{n(\sum x^2)-(\sum x)^2}$

$a = \dfrac{(1105)(220)-(32)(3405)}{6(220)-(32)^2}$

$a = \dfrac{243100-108960}{1320-1024} = \dfrac{134140}{296} = 453.176$

$b = \dfrac{n(\sum xy)-(\sum x)(\sum y)}{n(\sum x^2)-(\sum x)^2}$

11-43. continued

$b = \frac{6(3405)-(32)(1105)}{6(220)-(32)^2} = \frac{20430-35360}{296}$

$b = \frac{-14930}{296} = 50.439$

$y' = a + bx$
$y' = 453.176 - 50.439x$
$y' = 453.176 - 50.439(4) = \$251.42$

11-45.

$a = \frac{(\sum y)(\sum x^2)-(\sum x)(\sum xy)}{n(\sum x^2)-(\sum x)^2}$

$a = \frac{(22.1)(86890)-(832)(2321.1)}{8(86890)-(832)^2}$

$a = \frac{1920269-1931155.2}{695120-692224} = \frac{10886.2}{2896} = -3.759$

$b = \frac{n(\sum xy)-(\sum x)(\sum y)}{n(\sum x^2)-(\sum x)^2}$

$b = \frac{8(2321.1)-(832)(22.1)}{8(86890)-(832)^2}$

$b = \frac{18568.8-18387.2}{2986} = \frac{181.6}{2896} = 0.063$

$y' = a + bx$
$y' = -3.759 + 0.063x$
$y' = -3.759 + 0.063(104) = 2.793$

11-47.
Since r is not significant, the regression line should not be computed.

11-49.
Since r is not significant, the regression line should not be computed.

11-51.

$a = \frac{(\sum y)(\sum x^2)-(\sum x)(\sum xy)}{n(\sum x^2)-(\sum x)^2}$

$a = \frac{(2610)(653.11) - (67.5)(25,292)}{7(653.11) - 67.5^2} = -167.07$

$b = \frac{n(\sum xy)-(\sum x)(\sum y)}{n(\sum x^2)-(\sum x)^2}$

$b = \frac{7(25,292) - (67.5)(2610)}{7(653.11) - 67.5^2} = 55.99$

$y' = a + bx$
$y' = -167.07 + 55.99x$
$y' = \$336.84$

11-53.

$a = \frac{(\sum y)(\sum x^2)-(\sum x)(\sum xy)}{n(\sum x^2)-(\sum x)^2}$

11-53. continued

$a = \frac{(633)(65616)-(626)(66166)}{6(65616)-(626)^2} = 63.193$

$b = \frac{n(\sum xy)-(\sum x)(\sum y)}{n(\sum x^2)-(\sum x)^2}$

$b = \frac{6(66166)-(626)(633)}{6(65616)-(626)^2} = 0.405$

$y' = a + bx$
$y' = 63.193 + 0.405x$
$y' = 63.193 + 0.405(104) = 105.313$

11-55.

$a = \frac{(\sum y)(\sum x^2)-(\sum x)(\sum xy)}{n(\sum x^2)-(\sum x)^2}$

$a = \frac{(29)(187)-(31)(119)}{6(187)-(31)^2} = 10.770$

$b = \frac{n(\sum xy)-(\sum x)(\sum y)}{n(\sum x^2)-(\sum x)^2}$

$b = \frac{6(119)-(31)(29)}{6(187)-(31)^2} = -1.149$

$y' = a + bx$
$y' = 10.770 - 1.149x$
$y' = 10.770 - 1.149(4) = 6$

11-57.

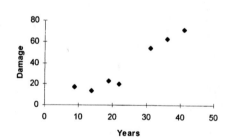

$\sum x = 172$
$\sum y = 262$
$\sum x^2 = 5060$
$\sum y^2 = 13340$
$\sum xy = 8079$
$n = 7$

$r = \frac{n(\sum xy)-(\sum x)(\sum y)}{\sqrt{[n(\sum x^2)-(\sum x)^2][n(\sum y^2)-(\sum y)^2]}}$

$r = \frac{7(8079)-(172)(262)}{\sqrt{[7(5060)-(172)^2][7(13340)-(262)^2]}} = 0.956$

$H_0: \rho = 0$
$H_1: \rho \neq 0$
C. V. = ± 0.754 d. f. = 5

11-57. continued
Decision: Reject
There is a significant relationship between the number of years a person smokes and the amount of lung damage.

$$a = \frac{(\sum y)(\sum x^2)-(\sum x)(\sum xy)}{n(\sum x^2)-(\sum x)^2}$$

$$a = \frac{(262)(5060)-(172)(8079)}{7(5060)-(172)^2} = -10.944$$

$$b = \frac{n(\sum xy)-(\sum x)(\sum y)}{n(\sum x^2)-(\sum x)^2}$$

$$b = \frac{7(8079)-(172)(262)}{7(5060)-(172)^2} = 1.969$$

$y' = a + bx$
$y' = -10.944 + 1.969x$
$y' = -10.944 + 1.969(30) = 48.126$

11-59.

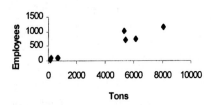

$\sum x = 26{,}728$
$\sum y = 4027$
$\sum x^2 = 162{,}101{,}162$
$\sum y^2 = 3{,}550{,}103$
$\sum xy = 23{,}663{,}669$
$n = 8$

$$r = \frac{n(\sum xy)-(\sum x)(\sum y)}{\sqrt{[n(\sum x^2)-(\sum x)^2]\,[n(\sum y^2)-(\sum y)^2]}}$$

$$r = \frac{8(23662669)-(26728)(4027)}{\sqrt{[8(162101162)-26728^2][8(3550103)-(4027)^2]}}$$

$r = 0.970$

$H_0:\ \rho = 0$
$H_1:\ \rho \neq 0$
C. V. $= \pm 0.707$ d. f. $= 6$

Decision: Reject.
There is a significant relationship between the number of tons of coal produced and the number of employees.

$$a = \frac{(\sum y)(\sum x^2)-(\sum x)(\sum xy)}{n(\sum x^2)-(\sum x)^2}$$

$$a = \frac{(4027)(162101162)-(26728)(23663669)}{8(162101162)-(26728)^2}$$

11-59. continued
a = 34.852

$$b = \frac{n(\sum xy)-(\sum x)(\sum y)}{n(\sum x^2)-(\sum x)^2}$$

$$b = \frac{8(23663669)-(26728)(4027)}{8(162101162)-(26728)^2} = 0.140$$

$y' = a + bx$
$y' = 34.852 + 0.140x$
$y' = 34.852 + 0.140(500) = 104.8$

11-61.

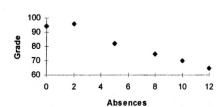

$\sum x = 37$
$\sum y = 482$
$\sum x^2 = 337$
$\sum y^2 = 39526$
$\sum xy = 2682$
$n = 6$

$$r = \frac{n(\sum xy)-(\sum x)(\sum y)}{\sqrt{[n(\sum x^2)-(\sum x)^2]\,[n(\sum y^2)-(\sum y)^2]}}$$

$$r = \frac{6(2682)-(37)(482)}{\sqrt{[6(337)-(37)^2][6(39526)-(482)^2]}}$$

$r = -0.981$

$H_0:\ \rho = 0$
$H_1:\ \rho \neq 0$
C. V. $= \pm 0.811$ d. f. $= 4$

Decision: Reject.
There is a significant negative relationship between the number of absences and the final grade.

$$a = \frac{(\sum y)(\sum x^2)-(\sum x)(\sum xy)}{n(\sum x^2)-(\sum x)^2}$$

$$a = \frac{(482)(337)-(37)(2682)}{6(337)-(37)^2} = 96.784$$

$$b = \frac{n(\sum xy)-(\sum x)(\sum y)}{n(\sum x^2)-(\sum x)^2}$$

$$b = \frac{6(2682)-(37)(482)}{6(337)-(37)^2} = -2.668$$

11-61. continued
$y' = a + bx$
$y' = 96.784 - 2.668x$

11-63.

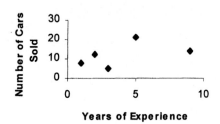

Years of Experience

$\sum x = 20$
$\sum y = 60$
$\sum x^2 = 120$
$\sum y^2 = 870$
$\sum xy = 278$
$n = 5$

$r = \dfrac{n(\sum xy) - (\sum x)(\sum y)}{\sqrt{[n(\sum x^2)-(\sum x)^2]\,[n(\sum y^2)-(\sum y)^2]}}$

$r = \dfrac{5(278) - (20)(60)}{\sqrt{5(120)-20^2][5(870)-60^2]}}$

$r = 0.491$

H_0: $\rho = 0$
H_1: $\rho \neq 0$
$t = 0.976$; $0.20 < \text{P-value} < 0.50$ (0.401)

Decision: Do not reject since P-value > 0.05. There is no significant relationship between the number of years of experience and the number of cars sold per month. Since r is not significant, no regression analysis should be done.

11-65.
For $11 - 15$
$\bar{x} = 5.3333$
$\bar{y} = 184.1667$
$b = -50.439$
$a = \bar{y} - b\bar{x}$
$a = 184.1667 - (-50.439)(5.3333)$
$a = 184.1667 + 269.0063$
$a = 453.173$ (differs due to rounding)

For $11 - 16$
$\bar{x} = 40.33$
$\bar{y} = 8.33$
$b = -0.317$
$a = \bar{y} - b\bar{x}$
$a = 8.33 - (-0.317)(40.33)$

11-65. continued
$a = 8.33 + 12.78$
$a = 21.11$ or 21.1

For $11 - 17$
$\bar{x} = 104$
$\bar{y} = 2.7625$
$b = 0.063$
$a = \bar{y} - b\bar{x}$
$a = 2.7625 - (0.063)(104)$
$a = 2.7625 - 6.552$
$a = -3.7895$ (differs due to rounding)

11-67.
Explained variation is the variation obtained from the predicted y' values, and is computed by $\sum (y' - \bar{y})^2$.

11-69.
Total variation is the sum of the explained and unexplained variation and is computed by $\sum (y - \bar{y})^2 = \sum (y' - \bar{y})^2 + \sum (y - y')^2$.

11-71.
It is found by squaring r.

11-73.
The coefficient of non-determination is $1 - r^2$.

11-75.
For $r = 0.70$, $r^2 = 0.49$, $1 - r^2 = 0.51$
49% of the variation of y is due to the variation of x, and 51% of the variation of y is due to chance.

11-77.
For $r = 0.37$, $r^2 = 0.1369$, $1 - r^2 = 0.8631$
13.69% of the variation of y is due to the variation of x, and 86.31% of the variation of y is due to chance.

11-79.
For $r = 0.05$, $r^2 = 0.0025$, $1 - r^2 = 0.9975$
0.25% of the variation of y is due to the variation of x, and 99.75% of the variation of y is due to chance.

11-81.
$S_{est} = \sqrt{\dfrac{\sum y^2 - a\sum y - b\sum xy}{n-2}}$

$S_{est} = \sqrt{\dfrac{141.25 - 10.499(22.5) - (-0.18)(625)}{6-2}}$

11-81. continued

$$S_{est} = \sqrt{4.380625}$$

$$s_{est} = 2.09$$

11-83.

$$S_{est} = \sqrt{\frac{\sum y^2 - a\sum y - b\sum xy}{n-2}} =$$

$$S_{est} = \sqrt{\frac{364525 - (453.176)(1105) - (-50.439)(3405)}{6-2}}$$

$$S_{est} = 94.22$$

11-85.

$y' = 10.499 - 0.18x$

$y' = 10.499 - 0.18(20)$

$y' = 6.899$

$$y' - t_{\frac{\alpha}{2}} \cdot S_{est}\sqrt{1 + \frac{1}{n} + \frac{n(x-\overline{X})}{n\sum x^2 - (\sum x)^2}} < y < y' +$$

$$t_{\frac{\alpha}{2}} \cdot S_{est}\sqrt{1 + \frac{1}{n} + \frac{n(x-\overline{X})^2}{n\sum x^2 - (\sum x)^2}}$$

$$6.899 - (2.132)(2.09)\sqrt{1 + \frac{1}{6} + \frac{6(20-37.5)^2}{6(9653)-225^2}}$$

$$< y < 6.899 +$$
$$(2.132)(2.09)\sqrt{1 + \frac{1}{6} + \frac{6(20-37.5)^2}{6(9653)-225^2}}$$

$6.899 - (2.132)(2.09)(1.191) < y < 6.899 +$
$\qquad (2.132)(2.09)(1.91)$

$1.59 < y < 12.21$

11-87.

$y' = 453.176 - 50.439x$

$y' = 453.176 - 50.439(4)$

$y' = 251.42$

$$y' - t_{\frac{\alpha}{2}} \cdot S_{est}\sqrt{1 + \frac{1}{n} + \frac{n(x-\overline{X})^2}{n\sum x^2 - (\sum x)^2}} < y <$$

$$y' + t_{\frac{\alpha}{2}} \cdot S_{est}\sqrt{1 + \frac{1}{n} + \frac{n(x-\overline{X})^2}{n\sum x^2 - (\sum x)^2}}$$

$$251.42 - 2.132(94.22)\sqrt{1 + \frac{1}{6} + \frac{6(4-5.33)^2}{6(220)-32^2}}$$

$$< y < 251.42 + 2.132(94.22)\sqrt{1 + \frac{1}{6} + \frac{6(4-5.33)^2}{6(220)-32^2}}$$

$251.42 - (2.132)(94.22)(1.1) < y <$
$\qquad 251.42 + (2.132)(94.22)(1.1)$

$30.46 < y < 472.38$

11-89.

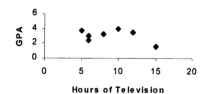

$\sum x = 62$

$\sum y = 21.4$

$\sum x^2 = 630$

$\sum y^2 = 69.5$

$\sum xy = 182.5$

$n = 7$

$$r = \frac{n(\sum xy) - (\sum x)(\sum y)}{\sqrt{[n(\sum x^2) - (\sum x)^2][n(\sum y^2) - (\sum y)^2]}}$$

$$r = \frac{7(182.5) - (62)(21.4)}{\sqrt{[7(630)-(62)^2][7(69.5)-(21.4)^2]}}$$

$r = -0.388$

$H_0: \rho = 0$

$H_1: \rho \neq 0$

C. V. $= \pm 0.875$ d. f. $= 5$

Decision: Do not reject. There is a not a significant relationship between the number of hours a person watches television and the person's grade point average. No regression should be done.

11-91.

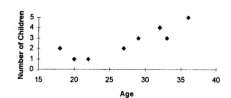

$\sum x = 217$

$\sum y = 21$

$\sum x^2 = 6187$

$\sum y^2 = 69$

$\sum xy = 626$

$n = 8$

$$r = \frac{n(\sum xy) - (\sum x)(\sum y)}{\sqrt{[n(\sum x^2) - (\sum x)^2][n(\sum y^2) - (\sum y)^2]}}$$

$$r = \frac{8(626) - (217)(21)}{\sqrt{[8(6187)-(217)^2][8(69)-(21)^2]}}$$

$r = 0.873$

11-91. continued

$H_0: \rho = 0$
$H_1: \rho \neq 0$
C. V. $= \pm 0.834$ d. f. $= 6$

Decision: Reject. There is a significant relationship between the mother's age and the number of children she has.

$a = \dfrac{(\sum y)(\sum x^2) - (\sum x)(\sum xy)}{n(\sum x^2) - (\sum x)^2}$

$a = \dfrac{(21)(6187) - (217)(626)}{8(6187) - (217)^2} = -2.457$

$b = \dfrac{n(\sum xy) - (\sum x)(\sum y)}{n(\sum x^2) - (\sum x)^2}$

$b = \dfrac{8(626) - (217)(21)}{8(6187) - (217)^2} = 0.187$

$y' = a + bx$
$y' = -2.457 + 0.187x$
$y' = -2.457 + 0.187(34) = 3.9$

11-93.

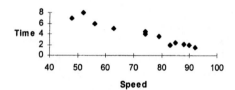

$\sum x = 884$
$\sum y = 47.8$
$\sum x^2 = 67728$
$\sum y^2 = 242.06$
$\sum xy = 3163.8$

n = 12

$r = \dfrac{n(\sum xy) - (\sum x)(\sum y)}{\sqrt{[n(\sum x^2) - (\sum x)^2][n(\sum y^2) - (\sum y)^2]}}$

$r = \dfrac{12(3163.8) - (884)(47.8)}{\sqrt{[12(67728) - (884)^2][12(242.06) - (47.8)^2]}}$

$r = -0.974$

$H_0: \rho = 0$
$H_1: \rho \neq 0$
C. V. $= \pm 0.708$ d. f. $= 10$

Decision: Reject the null. There is a significant relationship between speed and time.

$a = \dfrac{(\sum y)(\sum x^2) - (\sum x)(\sum xy)}{n(\sum x^2) - (\sum x)^2}$

11-93. continued

$a = \dfrac{(47.8)(67728) - (884)(3163.8)}{12(67728) - (884)^2}$

$a = 14.086$

$b = \dfrac{n(\sum xy) - (\sum x)(\sum y)}{n(\sum x^2) - (\sum x)^2}$

$b = \dfrac{12(3163.8) - (884)(47.8)}{12(67728) - (884)^2}$

$b = -0.137$

$y' = a + bx$
$y' = 14.086 - 0.137x$
$y' = 14.086 - 0.137(72) = 4.222$

11-95.

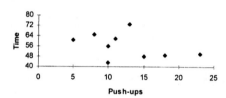

$\sum x = 113$
$\sum y = 507$
$\sum x^2 = 1657$
$\sum y^2 = 29309$
$\sum xy = 6198$
n = 9

$r = \dfrac{n(\sum xy) - (\sum x)(\sum y)}{\sqrt{[n(\sum x^2) - (\sum x)^2][n(\sum y^2) - (\sum y)^2]}}$

$r = \dfrac{9(6198) - (113)(507)}{\sqrt{[9(1657) - (113)^2][9(29309) - (507)^2]}}$

$r = -0.397$

$H_0: \rho = 0$
$H_1: \rho \neq 0$
C. V. $= \pm 0.798$ d. f. $= 7$

Decision: Do not reject. Since the null hypothesis is not rejected, no regression should be done.

11-97.

$S_{est} = \sqrt{\dfrac{\sum y^2 - a\sum y - b\sum xy}{n - 2}}$

$S_{est} = \sqrt{\dfrac{242.06 - 14.086(47.8) + 0.137(3163.8)}{12 - 2}}$

$S_{est} = \sqrt{\dfrac{2.1898}{10}} = \sqrt{0.21898} = 0.468$

11-99.

$y' = 14.086 - 0.137x$

$y\prime = 14.086 - 0.137(72) = 4.222$

$$y' - t_{\frac{\alpha}{2}} \cdot s_{est}\sqrt{1 + \frac{1}{n} + \frac{n(x-\overline{X})^2}{n\Sigma x^2 - (\Sigma x)^2}} < y <$$

$$y' + t_{\frac{\alpha}{2}} \cdot s_{est}\sqrt{1 + \frac{1}{n} + \frac{n(x-\overline{X})^2}{n\Sigma x^2 - (\Sigma x)^2}}$$

$$4.222 - 1.812(0.468)\sqrt{1 + \frac{1}{12} + \frac{12(72-73.667)^2}{12(67,728) - 884^2}}$$

$$< y < 4.222 + 1.812(0.468)\sqrt{1 + \frac{1}{12} + \frac{12(72-73.667)^2}{12(67,728) - 884^2}}$$

$4.222 - 1.812(0.468)(1.041) < y <$
$\qquad 4.222 + 1.812(0.468)(1.041)$

$3.34 < y < 5.10$

Quiz:

1. False, the y variable would decrease.
2. True
3. True
4. False, the relationship may be affected by another variable, or by chance.
5. False, a relationship may be caused by chance.
6. False, there are several independent variables and one dependent variable.
7. a
8. a
9. d
10. c
11. b
12. scatter diagram
13. independent
14. $-1, +1$
15. b
16. line of best fit
17. $+1, -1$

18.

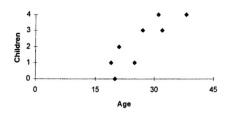

$\sum x = 213$
$\sum x^2 = 5985$
$\sum y = 18$
$\sum y^2 = 56$
$\sum xy = 539$
$n = 8$

18. continued

$r = 0.857$

$H_0: \rho = 0$ and $H_1: \rho \neq 0$. C.V. $= \pm 0.707$ and d. f. $= 6$. Reject. There is a significant relationship between father's age and number of children.

$a = -2.818 \qquad b = 0.19$

$y\prime = -2.818 + 0.19x$

For x = 35 years old:

$y\prime = -2.818 + 0.19(35) = 3.8$ or 4

19.

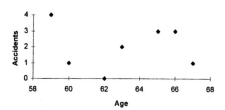

$\sum x = 442$
$\sum x^2 = 27,964$
$\sum y = 14$
$\sum y^2 = 40$
$\sum xy = 882$
$n = 7$
$r = -0.078$

$H_0: \rho = 0$ and $H_1: \rho \neq 0$. d. f. $= 5$ and C. V. $= \pm 0.764$. Decision: do not reject. There is not a significant relationship between age and number of accidents.

20.

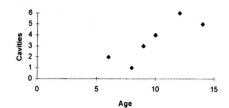

$\sum x = 59$
$\sum x^2 = 621$
$\sum y = 21$
$\sum y^2 = 91$
$\sum xy = 229$
$n = 6$
$r = 0.842$

$H_0: \rho = 0$ and $H_1: \rho \neq 0$; d. f. $= 4$ and C. V. $= \pm 0.811$. Decision: Reject. There is a significant relationship between age and number of cavities.

$a = -1.918 \qquad b = 0.551$

$y\prime = -1.918 + 0.551x$

20. continued

When x = 11: $y/ = -1.918 + 0.551(11)$

$y/ = 4.14 \approx 4$ cavities

21.

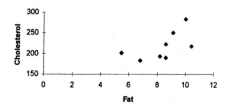

$\sum x = 67.2$

$\sum x^2 = 582.62$

$\sum y = 1740$

$\sum y^2 = 386,636$

$\sum xy = 14847.9$

n = 8

r = 0.602

H_0: $\rho = 0$ and H_1: $\rho \neq 0$; d. f. = 6 and C. V. = ± 0.707. Decision: Do not reject. There is no significant relationship between fat and cholesterol.

22.

$S_{est} = \sqrt{\frac{91 - (-1.918)(21) - 0.551(229)}{6-2}}$

$S_{est} = 1.13$

23.

(For calculation purposes only, since no regression should be done.)

$S_{est} = \sqrt{\frac{386,636 - 110.12(1740) - 12.784(14,847.9)}{8-2}}$

$S_{est} = 29.47$

24.

$y/ = -1.918 + 0.551(7) = 1.939$ or 2

$$2 - 2.132(1.129)\sqrt{1 + \frac{1}{6} + \frac{6(11-9.833)^2}{6(621) - 59^2}} < y$$

$$< 2 + 2.132(1.129)\sqrt{1 + \frac{1}{6} + \frac{6(11-9.833)^2}{6(621) - 59^2}}$$

$$2 - 2.132(1.129)(1.095) < y < 2 + 2.132(1.129)(1.095)$$

$$-0.6 < y < 4.6 \Rightarrow 0 < y < 5$$

25.

Since no regression should be done, the prediction interval is $\bar{y} = 217.5$, the average of the y values.

Note: Graphs are not to scale and are intended to convey a general idea. Answers may vary due to rounding.

12-1.
The variance test compares a sample variance to a hypothesized population variance, while the goodness of fit test compares a distribution obtained from a sample with a hypothesized distribution.

12-3.
The expected values are computed based on the null hypothesis.

12-5.
H_0: The number of accidents is equally distributed throughout the week. (claim)
H_1: The number of accidents is not equally distributed throughout the week.
C. V. = 12.592   d. f. = 6 $\alpha = 0.05$

$$E = \frac{189}{7} = 27$$

$$\chi^2 = \sum \frac{(O-E)^2}{E} = \frac{(28-27)^2}{27} + \frac{(32-27)^2}{27} +$$

$$\frac{(15-27)^2}{27} + \frac{(14-27)^2}{27} + \frac{(38-27)^2}{27} + \frac{(43-27)^2}{27}$$

$$+ \frac{(19-27)^2}{27} = 28.887$$

Alternate Solution:

O	E	O − E	$(O-E)^2$	$\frac{(O-E)^2}{E}$
28	27	1	1	0.037
32	27	5	25	0.926
15	27	-12	144	5.333
14	27	-13	169	6.259
38	27	11	121	4.481
43	27	16	256	9.481
19	27	-8	64	2.370
				28.887

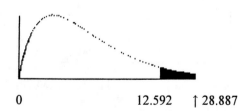

0   12.592   ↑ 28.887

Reject the null hypothesis. There is enough evidence to reject the claim that the number of accidents is equally distributed during the week.

12-7.
H_0: There is no preference for sherbet flavors. (claim)
H_1: There is a preference for sherbet flavors.
C. V. = 11.345   d. f. = 3 $\alpha = 0.01$

$$E = \frac{64}{4} = 16$$
$$\chi^2 = \sum \frac{(O-E)^2}{E} = \frac{(12-16)^2}{16} + \frac{(24-16)^2}{16}$$

$$+ \frac{(19-16)^2}{16} + \frac{(9-16)^2}{16} = 8.625$$

Alternate Solution:

O	E	O − E	$(O − E)^2$	$\frac{(O-E)^2}{E}$
12	16	-4	16	1.00
24	16	8	64	4.00
19	16	3	9	0.5625
9	16	-7	49	3.0625
				8.625

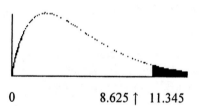

0   8.625 ↑   11.345

Do not reject the null hypothesis. There is not enough evidence to reject the claim that there is no preference for flavors.

12-9.
H_0: The blood types are distributed as follows: O - 42%, A - 44%, B - 10%, and AB - 4%. (claim)
H_1: The distribution of blood types is different from the null hypothesis.
C. V. = 6.251   d. f. = 3 $\alpha = 0.10$

$$E(A) = 44\% \cdot 200 = 88$$
$$E(O) = 42\% \cdot 200 = 84$$
$$E(B) = 10\% \cdot 200 = 20$$
$$E(AB) = 4\% \cdot 200 = 8$$

$$\chi^2 = \frac{(58-88)^2}{88} + \frac{(65-84)^2}{84} + \frac{(55-20)^2}{20}$$

$$+ \frac{(22-8)^2}{8} = 100.275$$

12-9. continued
Alternate Solution:

O	E	O − E	$(O - E)^2$	$\frac{(O-E)^2}{E}$
58	88	-30	900	10.227
65	84	-19	361	4.298
55	20	35	1225	61.25
22	8	14	196	24.5
				100.275

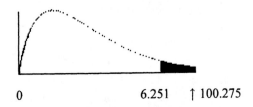

0　　　　　　　6.251　↑ 100.275

Reject the null hypothesis. There is enough evidence to reject the claim that the distribution of blood types is the same as the national distribution.

12-11.
H_0: The loans are distributed as follows: 21% for mortgages, 39% for autos, 20% unsecured, 12% for real estate, and 8% miscellaneous. (claim)
H_1: The distribution is different from that stated in the null hypothesis.
C. V. = ±9.488　　d. f. = 4　　$\alpha = 0.05$

$E(\text{Home}) = 21\% \cdot 100 = 21$
$E(\text{Auto}) = 39\% \cdot 100 = 39$
$E(\text{Unsecured}) = 20\% \cdot 100 = 20$
$E(\text{ Real Estate}) = 12\% \cdot 100 = 12$
$E(\text{Miscellaneous}) = 8\% \cdot 100 = 8$

$$\chi^2 = \frac{(25-21)^2}{21} + \frac{(44-39)^2}{39} + \frac{(19-20)^2}{20} +$$

$$\frac{(8-12)^2}{12} + \frac{(4-8)^2}{8} = 4.786$$

Alternate Solution:

O	E	O − E	$(O - E)^2$	$\frac{(O-E)^2}{E}$
25	21	4	16	0.7619
44	39	5	25	0.6410
19	20	-1	1	0.05
8	12	-4	16	1.3333
4	8	-4	16	2.0000
				4.7862

12-11. continued

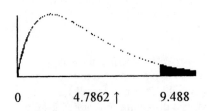

0　　　　　4.7862 ↑　　　　9.488

Do not reject the null hypothesis. There is not enough evidence to reject the claim that the distribution is the same as reported in the newspaper.

12-13.
H_0: The method of payment for purchases is distributed as follows: 53% cash, 30% checks, 16% credit cards, and 1% no preference. (claim)
H_1: The distribution is different from the null hypothesis.
C. V. = 11.345　　d. f. = 3　　$\alpha = 0.01$

$E(\text{cash}) = 53\% \text{ of } 800 = 424$
$E(\text{check}) = 30\% \text{ of } 800 = 240$
$E(\text{credit card}) = 16\% \text{ of } 800 = 128$
$E(\text{other}) = 1\% \text{ of } 800 = 8$

$$\chi^2 = \frac{(400-424)^2}{424} + \frac{(210-240)^2}{240} + \frac{(170-128)^2}{128}$$

$$+ \frac{(20-8)^2}{8} = 36.8898$$

Alternate Solution:

O	E	O − E	$(O - E)^2$	$\frac{(O-E)^2}{E}$
400	424	-24	576	1.3585
210	240	-30	900	3.7500
170	128	42	1764	13.7813
20	8	12	144	18.0000
				36.8898

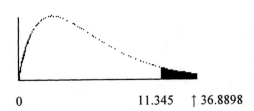

0　　　　　　　11.345　↑ 36.8898

Reject the null hypothesis. There is enough evidence to reject the claim that the distribution is the same as reported in the survey.

12-15.

H_0: The distribution of college majors is as follows: 40% Business, 25% Computer Science, 15% Science, 10% Social Science, 5% Liberal Arts and 5% General Studies. (claim)

H_1: The null hypothesis is not true.

C. V. = 9.236   d. f. = 5

E(Bus) = 40% of 200 = 80
E(CS) = 25% of 200 = 50
E(SC) = 15% of 200 = 30
E(SS) = 10% of 200 = 20
E(LA) = 5% of 200 = 10
E(GS) = 5% of 200 = 10

$$\chi^2 = \sum \frac{(O-E)^2}{E} = \frac{(72-80)^2}{80} + \frac{(53-50)^2}{50}$$

$$+ \frac{(32-30)^2}{30} + \frac{(20-20)^2}{20} + \frac{(16-10)^2}{10}$$

$$+ \frac{(7-10)^2}{10} = 5.613$$

Alternate Solution:

O	E	O − E	$(O-E)^2$	$\frac{(O-E)^2}{E}$
72	80	-8	64	0.800
53	50	3	9	0.180
32	30	2	4	0.133
20	20	0	0	0
16	10	6	36	3.600
7	10	-3	9	0.900
				5.613

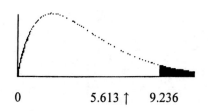

0   5.613 ↑   9.236

Do not reject the null hypothesis. There is not enough evidence to reject the dean's hypothesis.

12-17.

H_0: 50% of customers purchase word processing programs, 25% purchase spread sheet programs, and 25% purchase data base programs. (claim)

H_1: The null hypothesis is not true.

E(WP) = 50% · 80 = 40
E(SS) = 25% · 80 = 20

12-17. continued
E(DB) = 25% · 80 = 20

$$\chi^2 = \sum \frac{(O-E)^2}{E} = \frac{(38-40)^2}{40} + \frac{(23-20)^2}{20} +$$

$$\frac{(19-20)^2}{20} = 0.1 + 0.45 + 0.05 = 0.6$$

$\alpha = 0.05$ d. f. = 2
P-value > 0.10 (0.741)

Alternate Solution:

O	E	O − E	$(O-E)^2$	$\frac{(O-E)^2}{E}$
38	40	-2	4	0.1
23	20	3	9	0.45
19	20	-1	1	0.05
				0.60

Do not reject the null hypothesis since P-value > 0.05. There is not enough evidence to reject the store owner's assumption.

12-19.
Answers will vary.

12-21.
d. f. = (rows − 1)(columns − 1)

12-23.
H_0: The variables are independent or not related.

H_1: The variables are dependent or related.

12-25.
The expected values are computed as (row total · column total) ÷ grand total.

12-27.
H_0: $p_1 = p_2 = p_3 = \cdots = p_n$
H_1: At least one proportion is different from the others.

12-29.
H_0: Coffee consumption is independent of age.

H_1: Coffee consumption is dependent on age. (claim)

C. V. = 16.812   d. f. = 6

$$E = \frac{(\text{row sum})(\text{column sum})}{\text{grand total}}$$

$$E_{1,1} = \frac{(46)(45)}{152} = 13.618$$

$$E_{1,2} = \frac{(46)(52)}{152} = 15.737$$

12-29. continued

$E_{1,3} = \frac{(46)(55)}{152} = 16.645$

$E_{2,1} = \frac{(51)(45)}{152} = 15.099$

$E_{2,2} = \frac{(51)(52)}{152} = 17.447$

$E_{2,3} = \frac{(51)(55)}{152} = 18.454$

$E_{3,1} = \frac{(27)(45)}{152} = 7.993$

$E_{3,2} = \frac{(27)(52)}{152} = 9.237$

$E_{3,3} = \frac{(27)(55)}{152} = 9.770$

$E_{4,1} = \frac{(28)(45)}{152} = 8.289$

$E_{4,2} = \frac{(28)(52)}{152} = 9.579$

$E_{4,3} = \frac{(28)(55)}{152} = 10.132$

Coffee Consumption

Age	Low	Moderate	High	Total
21 – 30	18(13.618)	16(15.737)	12(16.645)	46
31 – 40	9(15.099)	15(17.447)	27(18.454)	51
41 – 50	5(7.993)	12(9.237)	10(9.770)	27
51 & up	13(8.289)	9(9.579)	6(10.132)	28
Total	45	52	55	152

$\chi^2 = \sum \frac{(O-E)^2}{E} = \frac{(18-13.618)^2}{13.618} + \frac{(16-15.737)^2}{15.737} +$

$\frac{(12-16.645)^2}{16.645} + \frac{(9-15.099)^2}{15.099} + \frac{(15-17.447)^2}{17.447}$

$+ \frac{(27-18.454)^2}{18.454} + \frac{(5-7.993)^2}{7.993} + \frac{(12-9.237)^2}{9.237} +$

$\frac{(10-9.770)^2}{9.770} + \frac{(13-8.289)^2}{8.289} + \frac{(9-9.579)^2}{9.579}$

$+ \frac{(6-10.132)^2}{10.132} = 15.824$

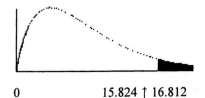

0   15.824 ↑ 16.812

Reject the null hypothesis. There is enough evidence to support the claim that coffee consumption is dependent upon the age of the individual.

12-31.

H_0: The price of the automobile is independent of the age of the purchaser.

H_1: The price of the automobile is dependent upon the age of the purchaser. (claim)

C. V. = 12.592   d. f. = 6

$E = \frac{(\text{row sum})(\text{column sum})}{\text{grand total}}$

$E_{1,1} = \frac{(44)(100)}{222} = 19.820$

$E_{1,2} = \frac{(44)(74)}{222} = 14.667$

$E_{1,3} = \frac{(44)(48)}{222} = 9.514$

$E_{2,1} = \frac{(82)(100)}{222} = 36.937$

$E_{2,2} = \frac{(82)(74)}{222} = 27.333$

$E_{2,3} = \frac{(82)(48)}{222} = 17.730$

$E_{3,1} = \frac{(64)(100)}{222} = 28.829$

$E_{3,2} = \frac{(64)(74)}{222} = 21.333$

$E_{3,3} = \frac{(64)(48)}{222} = 13.838$

$E_{4,1} = \frac{(32)(100)}{222} = 14.414$

$E_{4,2} = \frac{(32)(74)}{222} = 10.667$

$E_{4,3} = \frac{(32)(48)}{222} = 6.919$

Age	<$20K	$20-30K	$30-40K	Total
21-30	16(19.820)	25(14.667)	3(9.514)	44
31-40	44(36.937)	23(27.333)	15(17.730)	82
41-50	31(28.829)	15(21.333)	18(13.838)	64
51 +	9(14.414)	11(10.667)	12(6.919)	32
Total	100	74	48	222

$\chi^2 = \sum \frac{(O-E)^2}{E} = \frac{(16-19.820)^2}{19.820} + \frac{(25-14.667)^2}{14.667}$

$+ \frac{(3-9.514)^2}{9.514} + \frac{(44-36.937)^2}{36.937} + \frac{(23-27.333)^2}{27.333}$

$+ \frac{(15-17.730)^2}{17.730} + \frac{(31-28.829)^2}{28.829} + \frac{(15-21.333)^2}{21.333}$

$+ \frac{(18-13.838)^2}{13.838} + \frac{(9-14.414)^2}{14.414} + \frac{(11-10.667)^2}{10.667}$

$+ \frac{(12-6.919)^2}{6.919} = 24.004$

12-31. continued

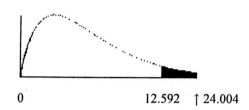

0   12.592 ↑ 24.004

Reject the null hypothesis. There is enough evidence to support the claim that the price of the automobile is dependent upon the age of the purchaser.

12-33.
H_0: The number of ads people think they've seen is independent of the person's gender.
H_1: The number of ads seen is dependent upon the person's gender. (claim)
C. V. = 13.277   d. f. = 4 $\alpha = 0.01$

$$E_{1,1} = \frac{(300)(95)}{510} = 55.882$$

$$E_{1,2} = \frac{(300)(110)}{510} = 64.706$$

$$E_{1,3} = \frac{(300)(144)}{510} = 84.706$$

$$E_{1,4} = \frac{(300)(84)}{510} = 49.412$$

$$E_{1,5} = \frac{(300)(77)}{510} = 45.294$$

$$E_{2,1} = \frac{(210)(95)}{510} = 39.118$$

$$E_{2,2} = \frac{(210)(110)}{510} = 45.294$$

$$E_{2,3} = \frac{(210)(144)}{510} = 59.294$$

$$E_{2,4} = \frac{(210)(84)}{510} = 34.588$$

$$E_{2,5} = \frac{(210)(77)}{510} = 31.706$$

Gender	1 - 30	31 - 50	51 - 100
Men	45(55.882)	60(64.706)	90(84.706)
Women	50(39.118)	50(45.294)	54(59.294)
Total	95	110	144

Gender	101 - 300	301 or more	Total
Men	54(49.412)	51(45.294)	300
Women	30(34.588)	26(31.706)	210
Total	84	77	510

12-33. continued

$$\chi^2 = \sum \frac{(O-E)^2}{E} = \frac{(45-55.882)^2}{55.882} + \frac{(60-64.706)^2}{64.706}$$

$$+ \frac{(90-84.706)^2}{84.706} + \frac{(54-49.412)^2}{49.412} + \frac{(51-45.294)^2}{45.294}$$

$$+ \frac{(50-39.118)^2}{39.118} + \frac{(50-45.294)^2}{45.294} + \frac{(54-59.294)^2}{59.294}$$

$$+ \frac{(30-34.588)^2}{34.588} + \frac{(26-31.706)^2}{31.706} = 9.562$$

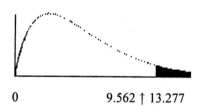

0   9.562 ↑ 13.277

Do not reject the null hypothesis. There is not enough evidence to support the claim that the number of ads people think they've seen or heard is related to the gender of the individual.

12-35.
H_0: The student's rating of the instructor is independent of the type of degree the instructor has.
H_1: The rating is dependent on the type of degree the instructor has. (claim)
C. V. = 7.779   d. f. = 4

$$E_{1,1} = \frac{(27)(33)}{86} = 10.360$$

$$E_{1,2} = \frac{(27)(26)}{86} = 8.163$$

$$E_{1,3} = \frac{(27)(27)}{86} = 8.477$$

$$E_{2,1} = \frac{(28)(33)}{86} = 10.744$$

$$E_{2,2} = \frac{(28)(26)}{86} = 8.465$$

$$E_{2,3} = \frac{(28)(27)}{86} = 8.791$$

$$E_{3,1} = \frac{(31)(33)}{86} = 11.895$$

$$E_{3,2} = \frac{(31)(26)}{86} = 9.372$$

$$E_{3,3} = \frac{(31)(27)}{86} = 9.733$$

12-35. continued

	BS	MS	PhD	Total
Excellent	14(11.616)	4(8.477)	9(8.163)	27
Average	16(10.744)	7(8.791)	5(8.465)	28
Poor	3(19.570)	16(9.733)	12(9.372)	31
	33	27	26	86

$$\chi^2 = \sum \frac{(O-E)^2}{E} = \frac{(14-10.360)^2}{10.360} + \frac{(9-8.163)^2}{8.163}$$

$$+ \frac{(4-8.477)^2}{8.477} + \frac{(16-10.744)^2}{10.744} + \frac{(5-8.465)^2}{8.465}$$

$$+ \frac{(7-8.791)^2}{8.791} + \frac{(3-11.895)^2}{11.895} + \frac{(12-9.372)^2}{9.372}$$

$$+ \frac{(16-9.733)^2}{9.733} = 19.507$$

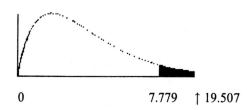

0   7.779   ↑ 19.507

Reject the null hypothesis. There is enough evidence to support the claim that the degree of the instructor is related to the students' opinions about instructors' effectiveness.

12-37.

H_0: The type of video rented by a person is independent of the person's age.
H_1: The type of video a person rents is dependent on the person's age. (claim)
C. V. = 13.362   d. f. = 8 $\alpha = 0.10$

Age	Doc.	Comedy	Mystery	Total
12-20	14(6.588)	9(13.433)	8(10.979)	31
21-29	15(8.075)	14(16.467)	9(13.458)	38
30-38	9(14.663)	21(29.9)	39(24.438)	69
39-47	7(9.775)	22(19.933)	17(16.292)	46
48 +	6(11.9)	38(24.267)	12(19.833)	56
Total	51	104	85	240

$$\chi^2 = \frac{(14-6.588)^2}{6.588} + \frac{(9-13.433)^2}{13.433} + \frac{(8-10.979)^2}{10.979}$$

$$+ \frac{(15-8.075)^2}{8.075} + \frac{(14-16.467)^2}{16.467} + \frac{(9-13.458)^2}{13.458}$$

$$+ \frac{(9-14.663)^2}{14.663} + \frac{(21-29.9)^2}{29.9} + \frac{(39-24.438)^2}{24.438}$$

$$+ \frac{(7-9.775)^2}{9.775} + \frac{(22-19.933)^2}{19.933} + \frac{(17-16.292)^2}{16.292}$$

$$+ \frac{(6-11.9)^2}{11.9} + \frac{(38-24.267)^2}{24.267} + \frac{(12-19.833)^2}{19.833} =$$

12-37. continued

$\chi^2 = 46.733$

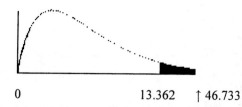

0   13.362   ↑ 46.733

Reject the null hypothesis. There is enough evidence to support the claim that the type of movie selected is related to the age of the customer.

12-39.

H_0: The type of snack purchased is independent of the gender of the consumer. (claim)
H_1: The type of snack purchased is dependent upon the gender of the consumer.
C. V. = 4.605   d. f. = 2

Gender	Hot Dog	Peanuts	Popcorn	Total
Male	12(13.265)	21(15.388)	19(23.347)	52
Female	13(11.735)	8(13.612)	25(20.653)	46
Total	25	29	44	98

$$\chi^2 = \sum \frac{(O-E)^2}{E} = \frac{(12-13.265)^2}{13.265} + \frac{(21-15.388)^2}{15.388}$$

$$+ \frac{(19-23.347)^2}{23.347} + \frac{(13-11.735)^2}{11.735} + \frac{(8-13.612)^2}{13.612}$$

$$+ \frac{(25-20.653)^2}{20.653} = 6.342$$

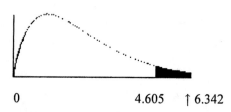

0   4.605   ↑ 6.342

Reject the null hypothesis. There is enough evidence to reject the claim that the type of snack chosen is independent of the gender of the individual.

12-41.

H_0: The type of book selected by the individual is independent of the gender of the indivicual. (claim)

12-41. continued

H_1: The type of book selected by the individual is dependent on the gender of the individual.

$\alpha = 0.05$ d. f. = 2

Gender	Mystery	Romance	Self-help	Total
Male	243(214.121)	201(198.260)	191(222.618)	635
Female	135(163.879)	149(151.740)	202(170.382)	486
Total	378	350	393	1121

$$\chi^2 = \sum \frac{(O-E)^2}{E} = \frac{(243-214.121)^2}{214.121} + \frac{(201-198.260)^2}{198.260}$$

$$+ \frac{(191-222.618)^2}{222.618} + \frac{(135-163.879)^2}{163.879}$$

$$+ \frac{(149-151.740)^2}{151.740} + \frac{(202-170.382)^2}{170.382} = 19.429$$

P-value < 0.005 (0.00006)
Reject the null hypothesis since P-value < 0.05. There is enough evidence to reject the claim that the type of book purchased is independent of gender.

12-43.

H_0: $p_1 = p_2 = p_3 = p_4$ (claim)
H_1: At least one proportion is different.

C. V. = 7.851   d. f. = 3

$$E(passed) = \frac{120(167)}{120} = 41.75$$

$$E(failed) = \frac{120(313)}{120} = 78.25$$

	Southside	West End	East Hills	Jefferson	Total
Passed	49(41.75)	38(41.75)	46(41.75)	34(41.75)	167
Failed	71(78.25)	82(78.25)	74(78.25)	86(78.25)	313
Total	120	120	120	120	480

$$\chi^2 = \frac{(49-41.75)^2}{41.75} + \frac{(38-41.75)^2}{41.75} + \frac{(46-41.75)^2}{41.75}$$

$$+ \frac{(34-41.75)^2}{41.75} + \frac{(71-78.25)^2}{78.25} + \frac{(82-78.25)^2}{78.25}$$

$$+ \frac{(74-78.25)^2}{78.25} + \frac{(86-78.25)^2}{78.25} = 5.317$$

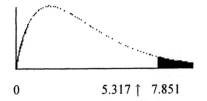

0   5.317 ↑ 7.851

Do not reject the null hypothesis. There is not enough evidence to reject the claim that the proportions are equal.

12-45.

H_0: $p_1 = p_2 = p_3 = p_4$ (claim)
H_1: At least one proportion is different.
C. V. = 7.815   d. f. = 3

$$E(yes) = \frac{107(86)}{344} = 26.75$$

$$E(no) = \frac{237(86)}{344} = 59.25$$

	21-29	30-39	40-49	50+	Total
Yes	32(26.75)	28(26.75)	26(26.75)	21(26.75)	107
No	54(59.25)	58(59.25)	60(59.25)	65(59.25)	237
Total	86	86	86	86	344

$$\chi^2 = \frac{(32-26.75)^2}{26.75} + \frac{(28-26.75)^2}{26.75} + \frac{(26-26.75)^2}{26.75} +$$

$$\frac{(21-26.75)^2}{26.75} + \frac{(54-59.25)^2}{59.25} + \frac{(58-59.25)^2}{59.25} + \frac{(60-59.25)^2}{59.25}$$

$$+ \frac{(65-59.25)^2}{59.25} = 3.40$$

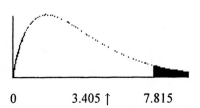

0   3.405 ↑   7.815

Do not reject the null hypothesis. There is not enough evidence to reject the claim that the proportions are the same.

12-47.

H_0: $p_1 = p_2 = p_3 = p_4$ (claim)
H_1: At least one proportion is different.
C. V. = 6.251   d. f. = 3

$$E(yes) = \frac{(100)(132)}{400} = 33$$

$$E(no) = \frac{(100)(268)}{400} = 67$$

	North	South	East	West	Total
Yes	43(33)	39(33)	22(33)	28(33)	132
No	57(67)	61(67)	78(67)	72(67)	268
Total	100	100	100	100	400

$$\chi^2 = \frac{(43-33)^2}{33} + \frac{(39-33)^2}{33} + \frac{(22-33)^2}{33} +$$

$$\frac{(28-33)^2}{33} + \frac{(57-67)^2}{67} + \frac{(61-67)^2}{67} + \frac{(78-67)^2}{67}$$

$$+ \frac{(72-67)^2}{67} = 12.755$$

12-47. continued

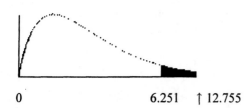

0   6.251   ↑ 12.755

Reject the null hypothesis. There is enough
evidence to reject the claim that the
proportions are the same.

12-49.
H_0: $p_1 = p_2 = p_3 = p_4$ (claim)
H_1: At least one proportion is different.

E(on bars) $= \frac{30(62)}{120} = 15.5$

E(not on bars) $= \frac{30(58)}{120} = 14.5$

	N	S	E	W	Total
on	15(15.5)	18(15.5)	13(15.5)	16(15.5)	62
off	15(14.5)	12(14.5)	17(14.5)	14(14.5)	58
Total	30	30	30	30	120

$\chi^2 = \frac{(15-15.5)^2}{15.5} + \frac{(18-15.5)^2}{15.5} + \frac{(13-15.5)^2}{15.5} +$

$\frac{(16-15.5)^2}{15.5} + \frac{(15-14.5)^2}{14.5} + \frac{(12-14.5)^2}{14.5} +$

$\frac{(17-14.5)^2}{14.5} + \frac{(14-14.5)^2}{14.5} = 1.734$

$\alpha = 0.05$ d. f. $= 3$
P-value > 0.10 (0.629)

Do not reject the null hypothesis. There is
not enough evidence to reject the claim that
the proportions are the same.

12-51.
H_0: $p_1 = p_2 = p_3$ (claim)
H_1: At least one proportion is different.
C. V. $= 4.605$ d. f. $= 2$

E(list) $= \frac{96(219)}{288} = 73$

E(no list) $= \frac{96(69)}{288} = 23$

	A	B	C	Total
list	77(73)	74(73)	68(73)	219
no list	19(23)	22((23)	28(23)	69
Total	96	96	96	288

12-51. continued
$\chi^2 = \frac{(77-73)^2}{73} + \frac{(74-73)^2}{73} + \frac{(68-73)^2}{73}$

$+ \frac{(19-23)^2}{23} + \frac{(22-23)^2}{23} + \frac{(28-23)^2}{23}$

$\chi^2 = 2.401$

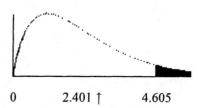

0   2.401 ↑   4.605

Do not reject the null hypothesis. There is
not enough evidence to reject the claim that
the proportions are the same.

12-53.
$\chi^2 = \frac{(|O-E|-0.5)^2}{E} = \frac{(|12-9.6|-0.5)^2}{9.6}$

$+ \frac{(|15-17.4|-0.5)^2}{17.4} + \frac{(|9-11.4|-0.5)^2}{11.4}$

$+ \frac{(|23-20.6|-0.5)^2}{20.6}$

$= \frac{3.61}{9.6} + \frac{3.61}{17.4} + \frac{3.61}{11.4} + \frac{3.61}{20.6}$

$= 0.376 + 0.207 + 0.317 + 0.175 = 1.075$

12-55.
The analysis of variance using the F-test can
be used to compare 3 or more means.

12-57.
The populations from which the samples
were obtained must be normally distributed.
The samples must be independent of each
other. The variances of the populations must
be equal.

12-59.
$F = \frac{s_B^2}{s_W^2}$

12-61.
One.

12-63.
H_0: $\mu_1 = \mu_2 = \mu_3$
H_1: At least one mean is different from the
    others.
C. V. $= 3.35$ $\alpha = 0.05$ d. f. $= 2, 27$

12-63. continued

$F = \frac{14.800}{1.985} = 7.456$

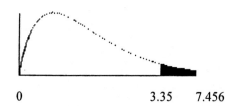

0   3.35   7.456

Reject. At least one mean is different from the others.

12-65.

H_0: $\mu_1 = \mu_2 = \mu_3$
H_1: At least one mean is different from the others.
C. V. = 3.55 $\alpha = 0.05$
d. f. N = 2   d. f. D = 18

$F = \frac{240.81}{12.64} = 19.05$

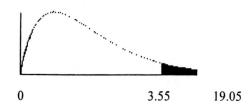

0   3.55   19.05

Reject. At least one mean is different from the others.

12-67.

H_0: $\mu_1 = \mu_2 = \mu_3$
H_1: At least one mean is different from the others.
k = 3   N = 20   dfN = 2   dfD = 17
CV = 2.64 $\alpha = 0.10$

$\overline{X}_1 = 449.143$ $s_1^2 = 6230.14$

$\overline{X}_2 = 440.444$ $s_2^2 = 27,868.96$

$\overline{X}_3 = 332.25$ $s_3^2 = 1793.52$

$\overline{X}_{GM} = 421.85$

$s_B^2 = \frac{7(449.14-421.85)^2}{2} + \frac{9(440.44-421.85)^2}{2} +$

$\frac{4(332.25-421.85)^2}{2} = 20,219.36$

$s_W^2 = \frac{6(6230.14)+8(27868.96)+3(1793.52)}{6+8+3}$

12-67. continued

$s_W^2 = 15,630.19$

$F = \frac{20219.36}{15630.19} = 1.29$

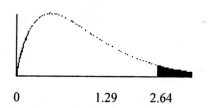

0   1.29   2.64

Do not reject the null hypothesis. There is not enough evidence to reject the claim that the means are the same.

12-69.

H_0: $\mu_1 = \mu_2 = \mu_3 = \mu_4$
H_1: At least one mean is different.
C. V. = 2.28 $\alpha = 0.10$
d. f. N = 3   d. f. D = 31

$\overline{X}_1 = 101.5$ $s_1 = 5.206$
$\overline{X}_2 = 69.125$ $s_2 = 3.523$
$\overline{X}_3 = 47.9$ $s_3 = 8.103$
$\overline{X}_4 = 22.909$ $s_4 = 5.907$

$\overline{X}_{GM} = \frac{1893}{35} = 54.09$

$s_B^2 = \frac{\sum n_i(\overline{X}_i - \overline{X}_{GM})^2}{k-1}$

$s_B^2 = \frac{6(101.5-54.09)^2}{3} + \frac{8(69.125-54.09)^2}{3}$

$+ \frac{10(47.9-54.09)^2}{3} + \frac{11(22.909-54.09)^2}{3}$

$s_B^2 = \frac{26,372.62}{3} = 8790.87$

$s_W^2 = \frac{\sum(n_i-1)s_i^2}{\sum(n_i-1)}$

$= \frac{5(5.206)^2+7(3.523)^2+9(8.103)^2+10(5.907)^2}{5+7+9+10}$

$= \frac{1162.25}{31} = 37.492$

$F = \frac{s_B^2}{s_W^2} = \frac{8790.87}{37.492} = 234.47$

Reject. At least one mean is different from the others.

12-71.

H_0: $\mu_1 = \mu_2 = \mu_3$
H_1: At least one mean is different from the others.

12-71. continued
C. V. = 2.61 $\alpha = 0.10$
d. f. N = 2   d. f. D = 19

$\overline{X}_1 = 233.33$ $s_1 = 28.225$
$\overline{X}_2 = 203.125$ $s_2 = 39.364$
$\overline{X}_3 = 155.625$ $s_3 = 28.213$

$\overline{X}_{GM} = 194.091$

$s_B^2 = \frac{\sum n_i(\overline{X}_i - \overline{X}_{GM})^2}{k-1}$

$s_B^2 = \frac{6(233.33-194.091)^2}{2} + \frac{8(203.125-194.091)^2}{2}$

$+ \frac{8(155.625-194.091)^2}{2} = 10{,}864.083$

$s_W^2 = \frac{\sum(n_i-1)s_i^2}{\sum(n_i-1)}$

$s_W^2 = \frac{5(28.225)^2+7(39.364)^2+7(28.213)^2}{5+7+7}$
$= 1073.776$

$F = \frac{s_B^2}{s_W^2} = \frac{10{,}864.083}{1073.776} = 10.12$

Reject. At least one mean is different from the others.

12-73.
$H_0: \mu_1 = \mu_2 = \mu_3 = \mu_4$
H_1: At least one mean is different.
C. V. = 5.29 $\alpha = 0.01$
d. f. N = 3   d. f. D = 16

$F = \frac{102.450}{8.775} = 11.675$

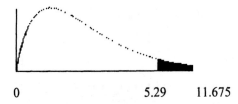

0   5.29   11.675

Reject. At least one mean is different from the others.

12-75.
H_0: The ad produced the same number of responses in each county. (claim)
H_1: The null hypothesis is not true.
C. V. = 11.345   d. f. = 3

$E = \frac{298}{4} = 74.5$

12-75. continued
$\chi^2 = \frac{(87-74.5)^2}{74.5} + \frac{(62-74.5)^2}{74.5}$

$+ \frac{(56-74.5)^2}{74.5} + \frac{(93-74.5)^2}{74.5} = 13.38$

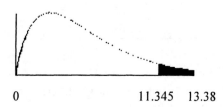

0   11.345   13.38

Reject the null hypothesis. There is enough evidence to reject the claim that the ad produced the same number of responses in each county.

12-77.
H_0: The condiment preference is independent of the sex of the purchaser. (claim)
H_1: The condiment preference is dependent on the sex of the purchaser.
C. V. = 4.605   d. f. = 2

	Relish	Catsup	Mustard	Total
Men	15(19.11)	18(15.29)	10(8.60)	43
Women	25(20.89)	14(16.71)	8(9.60)	47
Total	40	32	18	90

$\chi^2 = \sum \frac{(O-E)^2}{E} = \frac{(15-19.11)^2}{19.11} + \frac{(18-15.29)^2}{15.29}$

$+ \frac{(10-8.60)^2}{8.60} + \frac{(25-20.89)^2}{20.89} + \frac{(14-16.71)^2}{16.71}$

$+ \frac{(8-9.40)^2}{9.40} = 3.050$

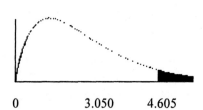

0   3.050   4.605

Do not reject the null hypothesis. There is not enough evidence to reject the claim that the condiment chosen is independent of the gender of the individual.

12-79.
H_0: The type of pet a person purchases is independent of the gender of the purchaser.

12-79. continued

H_1: The type of pet a person purchases is dependent upon the gender of the purchaser. (claim)

C. V. = 4.605   d. f. = 2 $\alpha = 0.10$

	Dog	Cat	Bird	Total
Males	32(37.5)	27(21.136)	16(16.364)	75
Females	23(17.5)	4(9.864)	8(7.636)	35
Total	55	31	24	90

$$\chi^2 = \sum \frac{(O-E)^2}{E} = \frac{(32-37.5)^2}{37.5} + \frac{(27-21.136)^2}{21.136}$$

$$+ \frac{(16-16.364)^2}{16.364} + \frac{(23-17.5)^2}{17.5} + \frac{(4-9.864)^2}{9.864}$$

$$+ \frac{(8-7.636)^2}{7.636} = 7.674$$

0   4.605   7.674

Reject the null hypothesis. There is enough evidence to support the claim that the type of pet purchased is related to the gender of the purchaser.

12-81.

H_0: $p_1 = p_2 = p_3 = p_4$ (claim)

H_1: At least one proportion is different.

C. V. = 7.815   d. f. = 3

$$E(male) = \frac{100(219)}{400} = 54.75$$

$$E(female) = \frac{100(181)}{400} = 45.25$$

	May	June	July	Aug	Total
Male	51(54.75)	47(54.75)	58(54.75)	63(54.75)	219
Female	49(45.25)	53(45.25)	42(45.25)	37(45.25)	181
Total	100	100	100	100	400

$$\chi^2 = \frac{(51-54.75)^2}{54.75} + \frac{(47-54.75)^2}{54.75} + \frac{(58-54.75)^2}{54.75}$$

$$+ \frac{(63-54.75)^2}{54.75} + \frac{(49-45.25)^2}{45.25} + \frac{(53-45.25)^2}{45.25} +$$

$$\frac{(42-45.25)^2}{45.25} + \frac{(37-45.25)^2}{45.25} = 6.17$$

12-81. continued

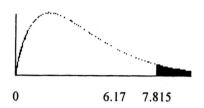

0   6.17   7.815

Do not reject the null hypothesis. There is not enough evidence to reject the claim that the proportions are the same.

12-83.

H_0: $p_1 = p_2 = p_3$ (claim)

H_1: At least one proportion is different.

C. V. = 9.210   d. f. = 2

$$E(yes) = \frac{200(186)}{600} = 62$$

$$E(no) = \frac{200(414)}{600} = 138$$

	#1	#2	#3	Total
Yes	87(62)	56(62)	43(62)	186
No	113(138)	144(138)	157(138)	414
	200	200	200	600

$$\chi^2 = \frac{(87-62)^2}{62} + \frac{(56-62)^2}{62} + \frac{(43-62)^2}{62}$$

$$+ \frac{(113-138)^2}{138} + \frac{(144-138)^2}{138} + \frac{(157-138)^2}{138}$$

$$\chi^2 = 23.89$$

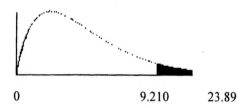

0   9.210   23.89

Reject the null hypothesis. There is not enough evidence to support the claim that the proportions are the same.

12-85.

H_0: $\mu_1 = \mu_2 = \mu_3$

H_1: At least one mean is different from the others. (claim)

C. V. = 3.81 $\alpha = 0.05$

d. f.N = 2   d. f. D = 13

12-85. continued

$$\overline{X}_1 = 106.286 \quad s_1 = 73.234$$

$$\overline{X}_2 = 97.0 \quad s_2 = 22.804$$

$$\overline{X}_3 = 73.0 \quad s_3 = 12.910$$

$$\overline{X}_{GM} = \frac{1521}{16} = 95.06$$

$$s_B^2 = \frac{\sum n_i(\overline{X}_i - \overline{X}_{GM})^2}{k-1}$$

$$= \frac{7(106.286-95.06)^2}{2} + \frac{5(97-95.06)^2}{2}$$

$$+ \frac{4(73-95.06)^2}{2} = 1423.78$$

$$s_W^2 = \frac{\sum(n_i-1)s_i^2}{\sum(n_i-1)}$$

$$= \frac{6(73.234)^2+4(22.804)^2+3(12.910)^2}{6+4+3}$$

$$= 2673.8$$

$$F = \frac{s_B^2}{s_W^2} = \frac{1423.78}{2673.8} = 0.532$$

Do not reject the null hypothesis. There is not enough evidence to support the claim that the means are different.

12-87.

H_0: $\mu_1 = \mu_2 = \mu_3$
H_1: At least one mean is different from the others.
C. V. = 3.89 $\quad \alpha = 0.05$
d. f. N = 2 $\quad$ d. f. D = 12

$$\overline{X}_1 = 26 \quad \overline{X}_2 = 10.429 \quad \overline{X}_3 = 17.5$$

$$s_1^2 = 50 \quad s_2^2 = 34.95 \quad s_3^2 = 83$$

$$\overline{X}_{GM} = \frac{\sum X}{N} = \frac{247}{15} = 16.467$$

$$s_B^2 = \frac{\sum n_i(\overline{X}_i - \overline{X}_{GM})^2}{k-1}$$

$$= \frac{4(26-16.467)^2 + 7(10.429-16.467)^2}{3-1}$$

$$+ \frac{4(17.5-16.467)^2}{3-1} = 311.5$$

$$s_W^2 = \frac{\sum(n_i-1)s_i^2}{\sum(n_i-1)}$$

$$= \frac{3(50) + 6(34.95) + 3(83)}{3+6+3} = 50.726$$

12-87. continued

$$F = \frac{s_B^2}{s_W^2} = \frac{311.5}{50.726} = 6.141$$

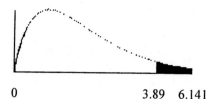

0 $\qquad$ 3.89 $\quad$ 6.141

Reject. At least one mean is different from the others.

12-89.

H_0: $\mu_1 = \mu_2 = \mu_3$
H_1: At least one mean is different from the others.
C. V. = 3.89 $\quad \alpha = 0.05$
d. f. N = 2 $\quad$ d. f. D = 12

$$\overline{X}_1 = 74 \quad \overline{X}_2 = 65.8 \quad \overline{X}_3 = 90.6$$

$$s_1^2 = 368 \quad s_2^2 = 258.7 \quad s_3^2 = 25.3$$

$$\overline{X}_{GM} = \frac{\sum X}{n} = \frac{1152}{15} = 76.8$$

$$s_B^2 = \frac{\sum n_i(\overline{X}_i - \overline{X}_{GM})^2}{k-1}$$

$$= \frac{5(74-76.8)^2 + 5(65.8-76.8)^2}{3-1}$$

$$+ \frac{5(90.6-76.8)^2}{3-1} = 798.2$$

$$s_W^2 = \frac{\sum(n_i-1)s_i^2}{\sum(n_i-1)}$$

$$= \frac{4(368) + 4(258.7) + 4(25.3)}{4+4+4} = 217.333$$

$$F = \frac{s_B^2}{s_W^2} = \frac{798.2}{217.333} = 3.673$$

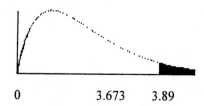

0 $\qquad$ 3.673 $\quad$ 3.89

Do not reject the null hypothesis. There is not enough evidence to conclude that there is a difference in the means.

12-91.

H_0: $\mu_1 = \mu_2 = \mu_3$

H_1: At least one mean is different from the others.

C. V. = 6.36 $\alpha = 0.01$

d. f. N = 2   d. f. D = 15

$F = \frac{25.287}{9.353} = 2.704$

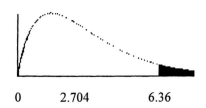

0   2.704   6.36

Do not reject.

Quiz:
1. False, it is one-tailed right.
2. True
3. False, there is little agreement between observed and expected frequencies.
4. False, there could be a significant difference between only some of the means.
5. False, degrees of freedom are used to find the critical value.
6. False, the null hypothesis should not be rejected.
7. c
8. b
9. d
10. d
11. a
12. a
13. 6
14. independent
15. right
16. at least five
17. ANOVA

18. H_0: The number of advertisements is equally distributed over five geographic regions.

H_1: The number of advertisements is not equally distributed over five regions.

C. V. = 9.488   d. f. = 4   E = 240.4

$\chi^2 = \sum \frac{(O-E)^2}{E} = 45.4$

Reject the null hypothesis. There is enough evidence to reject the claim that the number of advertisements is equally distributed.

19. H_0: The ads produced the same number of responses. (claim)

19. continued

H_1: The ads produced different numbers of responses.

C. V. = 13.277   d. f. = 4   E = 64.6

$\chi^2 = \sum \frac{(O-E)^2}{E} = 12.6$

Do not reject the null hypothesis. There is not enough evidence to reject the claim that the ads produced the same number of responses.

20. H_0: 48% of the customers order hamburgers, 33% order chicken, 19% order salad. (claim)

H_1: The distribution is not the same as stated in the null hypothesis.

C. V. = 5.991   d. f. = 2

$\chi^2 = 4.6$

Do not reject the null hypothesis. There is not enough evidence to reject the manager's claim.

21. H_0: Each gift was purchased with the same frequency. (claim)

H_1: The gifts were not purchased with the same frequency.

C. V. = 9.21   d. f. = 2

$\chi^2 = 73.1$

Reject the null hypothesis. There is enough evidence to reject the claim that the gifts were purchased with the same frequency.

22. H_0: The type of novel purchased is independent of the gender of the purchaser. (claim)

H_1: The type of novel purchased is dependent on the gender of the purchaser.

C. V. = 5.991   d. f. = 2

$\chi^2 = 132.9$

Reject the null hypothesis. There is enough evidence to reject the claim that the novel purchased is independent of the gender of the purchaser.

23. H_0: The type of pizza ordered is independent of the age of the purchaser. (claim)

H_1: The type of pizza ordered is dependent on the age of the purchaser.

C. V. = 14.684   d. f. = 9

$\chi^2 = 107.3$

Reject the null hypothesis. There is enough evidence to reject the claim that the type of pizza is independent of the age of the purchaser.

24. H_0: The color of the pennant purchased is independent of the gender of the purchaser. (claim)
H_1: The color of the pennant purchased is dependent on the gender of the purchaser.
C. V. $= 4.605$ d. f. $= 2$
$\chi^2 = 5.6$
Reject the null hypothesis. There is enough evidence to reject the claim that the color of the pennant purchased is independent of the gender of the purchaser.

25. H_0: $\mu_1 = \mu_2 = \mu_3$ (claim)
H_1: At least one mean is different from the others.
C. V. $= 3.55$
$s_B^2 = 785.333$ $s_W^2 = 6607.238$
$F = \frac{785.333}{6607.238} = 0.119$
Do not reject.

26. H_0: $\mu_1 = \mu_2 = \mu_3 = \mu_4$ (claim)
H_1: At least one mean is different from the others.
C. V. $= 3.10$
$s_B^2 = 42.37$ $s_W^2 = 10.125$
$F = \frac{42.37}{10.125} = 4.185$
Reject H_0. At least one mean is different from the others.

27. H_0: $\mu_1 = \mu_2 = \mu_3$
H_1: At least one mean is different from the others. (claim)
C. V. $= 6.36$ $\alpha = 0.01$
$s_B^2 = 4.936$ $s_W^2 = 6.975$
$F = 0.71$
Do not reject H_0. There is not enough evidence to show there is a difference in the means.

28. H_0: $\mu_1 = \mu_2 = \mu_3$
H_1: At least one mean is different from the others. (claim)
C. V. $= 3.63$ $\alpha = 0.05$
$s_B^2 = 13.379$ $s_W^2 = 271.486$
$F = 0.049$
Reject H_0. At least one mean is different from the others.

29. H_0: $\mu_1 = \mu_2 = \mu_3$
H_1: At least one mean is different from the others. (claim)
C. V. $= 3.89$ $\alpha = 0.05$
$s_B^2 = 3913.87$ $s_W^2 = 78.767$
$F = 49.689$

29. continued
Reject H_0. At least one mean is different from the others.

A-1. $9! = 9 \cdot 8 \cdot 7 \cdot 6 \cdot 5 \cdot 4 \cdot 3 \cdot 2 \cdot 1 =$ 362,880

A-2. $7! = 7 \cdot 6 \cdot 5 \cdot 4 \cdot 3 \cdot 2 \cdot 1 = 5040$

A-3. $5! = 5 \cdot 4 \cdot 3 \cdot 2 \cdot 1 = 120$

A-4. $0! = 1$

A-5. $1! = 1$

A-6. $3! = 3 \cdot 2 \cdot 1 = 6$

A-7. $\frac{12!}{9!} = \frac{12 \cdot 11 \cdot 10 \cdot 9!}{9!} = 1320$

A-8. $\frac{10!}{2!} = \frac{10 \cdot 9 \cdot 8 \cdot 7 \cdot 6 \cdot 5 \cdot 4 \cdot 3 \cdot 2!}{2!}$

$= 1,814,400$

A-9. $\frac{5!}{3!} = \frac{5 \cdot 4 \cdot 3!}{3!} = 20$

A-10. $\frac{11!}{7!} = \frac{11 \cdot 10 \cdot 9 \cdot 8 \cdot 7!}{7!} = 7920$

A-11. $\frac{9!}{(4!)(5!)} = \frac{9 \cdot 8 \cdot 7 \cdot 6 \cdot 5!}{4 \cdot 3 \cdot 2 \cdot 1 \cdot 5!} = 126$

A-12. $\frac{10!}{(7!)(3!)} = \frac{10 \cdot 9 \cdot 8 \cdot 7!}{3 \cdot 2 \cdot 1 \cdot 7!} = 120$

A-13. $\frac{8!}{4!4!} = \frac{8 \cdot 7 \cdot 6 \cdot 5 \cdot 4!}{4 \cdot 3 \cdot 2 \cdot 1 \cdot 4!} = 70$

A-14. $\frac{15!}{12!3!} = \frac{15 \cdot 14 \cdot 13 \cdot 12!}{3 \cdot 2 \cdot 1 \cdot 12!} = 455$

A-15. $\frac{10!}{(10!)(0!)} = \frac{10!}{10! \cdot 1} = 1$

A-16. $\frac{5!}{3!2!1!} = \frac{5 \cdot 4 \cdot 3!}{3! \cdot 2 \cdot 1 \cdot 1} = 10$

A-17. $\frac{8!}{3!3!2!} = \frac{8 \cdot 7 \cdot 6 \cdot 5 \cdot 4 \cdot 3!}{3! \cdot 3 \cdot 2 \cdot 1 \cdot 2 \cdot 1} = 560$

A-18. $\frac{11!}{7!2!2!} = \frac{11 \cdot 10 \cdot 9 \cdot 8 \cdot 7!}{7! \cdot 2 \cdot 1 \cdot 2 \cdot 1} = 1980$

A-19. $\frac{10!}{3!2!5!} = \frac{10 \cdot 9 \cdot 8 \cdot 7 \cdot 6 \cdot 5!}{3 \cdot 2 \cdot 1 \cdot 2 \cdot 1 \cdot 5!} = 2520$

A-20. $\frac{6!}{2!2!2!} = \frac{6 \cdot 5 \cdot 4 \cdot 3 \cdot 2!}{2 \cdot 1 \cdot 2 \cdot 1 \cdot 2!} = 90$

A-21.

X	X^2	$X - \overline{X}$	$(X - \overline{X})^2$
9	81	-3.1	9.61
17	289	4.9	24.01
32	1024	19.9	396.01
16	256	3.9	15.21
8	64	-4.1	16.81
2	4	-10.1	102.01
9	81	-3.1	9.61
7	49	-5.1	26.01
3	9	-9.1	82.81
18	324	5.9	34.81
121	2181		716.9

$\sum X = 121 \quad \overline{X} = \frac{121}{10} = 12.1 \quad \sum X^2 = 2181$

$(\sum X)^2 = 121^2 = 14641 \quad \sum (X - \overline{X})^2 = 716.9$

A-22.

X	X^2	$X - \overline{X}$	$(X - \overline{X})^2$
4	16	-3	9
12	144	5	25
9	81	2	4
13	169	6	36
0	0	-7	49
6	36	-1	1
2	4	-5	25
10	100	3	9
56	550		158

$\sum X = 56 \quad \overline{X} = \frac{56}{8} = 7 \quad \sum X^2 = 550$

$(\sum X)^2 = 56^2 = 3136 \quad \sum (X - \overline{X})^2 = 158$

A-23.

X	X^2	$X - \overline{X}$	$(X - \overline{X})^2$
5	25	-1.4	1.96
12	144	5.6	31.36
8	64	1.6	2.56
3	9	-3.4	11.56
4	16	-2.4	5.76
32	258		53.20

$\sum X = 32 \quad \overline{X} = \frac{32}{5} = 6.4 \quad \sum X^2 = 258$

$(\sum X)^2 = 32^2 = 1024 \quad \sum (X - \overline{X})^2 = 53.2$

A-24.

X	X^2	$X - \overline{X}$	$(X - \overline{X})^2$
6	36	-12.75	163.5625
2	4	-16.75	280.5625
18	324	-0.75	0.5625
30	900	11.25	126.5625
31	961	12.25	150.0625
42	1764	23.25	540.5625
16	256	-2.75	7.5625
5	25	-13.75	189.0625
150	4270		1457.5000

$\sum X = 150 \quad \overline{X} = \frac{150}{8} = 18.75 \quad \sum X^2 = 4270$

$(\sum X)^2 = 150^2 = 22500 \quad \sum(X-\overline{X})^2 = 1457.5$

A-25.

X	X^2	$X - \overline{X}$	$(X - \overline{X})^2$
80	6400	14.4	207.36
76	5776	10.4	108.16
42	1764	-23.6	556.96
53	2809	-12.6	158.76
77	5929	11.4	129.96
328	22678		1161.20

$\sum X = 328 \quad \overline{X} = \frac{328}{5} = 65.6 \quad \sum X^2 = 22678$

$(\sum X)^2 = 328^2 = 107584 \quad \sum(X-\overline{X})^2 = 1161.2$

A-26.

X	X^2	$X - \overline{X}$	$(X - \overline{X})^2$
123	15129	-15.17	230.1289
132	17424	-6.17	38.0689
216	46656	77.83	6057.5089
98	9604	-40.17	1613.6289
146	21316	7.83	61.3089
114	12996	-24.17	584.1889
829	123125		8584.8334

$\sum X = 829 \quad \overline{X} = \frac{829}{6} = 138.17$

$\sum X^2 = 123125 \quad (\sum X)^2 = 829^2 = 687241$

$\sum(X-\overline{X})^2 = 8584.8334$

A-27.

X	X^2	$X - \overline{X}$	$(X - \overline{X})^2$
53	2809	-16.3	265.69
72	5184	2.7	7.29
81	6561	11.7	136.89
42	1764	-27.3	745.29
63	3969	-6.3	39.69
71	5041	1.7	2.89
73	5329	3.7	13.69
85	7225	15.7	246.49
98	9604	28.7	823.69
55	3025	-14.3	204.49
693	50511		2486.10

$\sum X = 693 \quad \overline{X} = \frac{693}{10} = 69.3 \quad \sum X^2 = 50511$

$(\sum X)^2 = 693^2 = 480249 \quad \sum(X-\overline{X})^2 = 2486.1$

A-28.

X	X^2	$X - \overline{X}$	$(X - \overline{X})^2$
43	1849	-38.8	1505.44
32	1024	-49.8	2480.04
116	13456	34.2	1169.64
98	9604	16.2	262.44
120	14400	38.2	1459.24
409	40333		6876.80

$\sum X = 409 \quad \overline{X} = \frac{409}{5} = 81.8 \quad \sum X^2 = 40333$

$(\sum X)^2 = 409^2 = 167281 \quad \sum(X-\overline{X})^2 = 6876.8$

A-29.

X	X^2	$X - \overline{X}$	$(X - \overline{X})^2$
12	144	-41	1681
52	2704	-1	1
36	1296	-17	289
81	6561	28	784
63	3969	10	100
74	5476	21	441
318	20150		3296

$\sum X = 318 \quad \overline{X} = \frac{318}{6} = 53 \quad \sum X^2 = 20150$

$(\sum X)^2 = 318^2 = 101124 \quad \sum(X-\overline{X})^2 = 3296$

A-30.

X	X²	X − X̄	(X − X̄)²
− 9	81	− 5.67	32.1489
− 12	144	− 8.67	75.1689
18	324	21.33	454.9689
0	0	3.33	11.0889
− 2	4	1.33	1.7689
− 15	225	− 11.67	136.1889
− 20	778		711.3334

$\bar{X} = \frac{-20}{6} = -3.33$ $(\sum X)^2 = -20^2 = 400$

A-3

A-31.

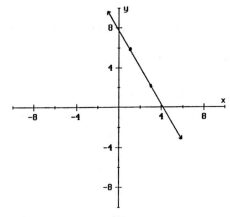

A-32.

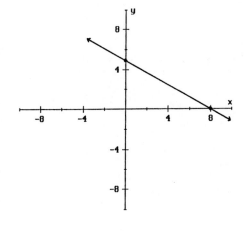

A-33.

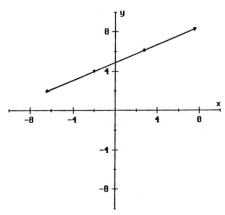

A-34.

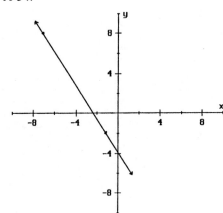

A-35.

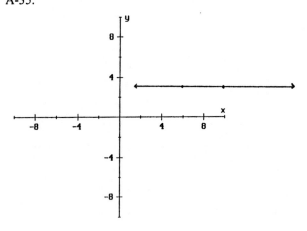

A-36.

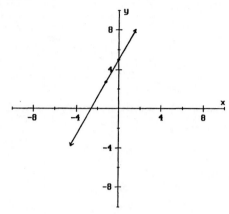

Two points are: (0, 5) and (-1, 3).

A-39.

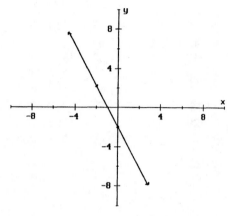

Two points are: (-2, 2) and (0, -2).

A-37.

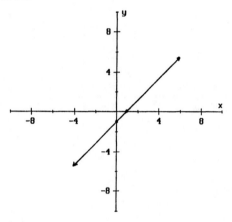

Two points are: (1, 0) and (0, -1).

A-40.

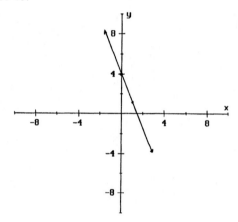

Two points are: (1, 1) and (0, 4)

A-38.

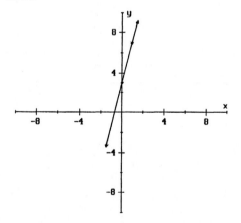

Two points are: (1, 7) and (0, 3).